# Professional Notary Records Book™

## Meets or exceeds the requirements of all states

Printed in the USA

| | |
|---|---|
| Notary Name: | |
| Notary Address: | |
| Phone: | Email Address: |
| Date of Notary Commission: | |
| State / Commission Jurisdiction: | |
| Commission / License Number: | |

**Date Range of Notary Actions Covered in this Journal:**

| Start Date: | End Date: |
|---|---|
| | |

Be aware that some states require that all of your notary records, including this Professional Notary Records Book, be turned over to the clerk of the county in which the notary has last taken the oath of office. In many cases this is also true should the notary fail to renew his or her commission or if for any reason he or she is removed from office, including because of the death of the notary.

ISBN: 978-0-578-22614-9

# NOTARY CHECKLIST

- Be sure to inspect the proper identification from all document signers.

- Examine the document to be notarized. Check to see if there have been any alterations and that no blanks are left unfilled. If there are any blanks, strike them out and have the signer(s) initial them. A notary has the right and the obligation to scan the document and to read portions of it in order to perform his/her duty in connection with the notarization but does not have a duty to read all of or to completely understand the document to be notarized.

- Determine whether or not the signer understands the document. Signer must understand the intention of the document before notarization may take place. If necessary, read (do not explain. Explaining the document may constitute "practicing law without a license" ) the document to any signer who cannot read, does not appear to understand, or is disabled.

- Be sure the date of the signature is not later than the date of the notarization. You should also verify that all document signers appear before the notary. If all parties cannot be present, your certificate should reflect exactly which parties appeared before you. Those not present will need to obtain a separate certificate for their signatures.

- Have all parties sign your record book exactly as they signed or will sign the document(s).

- Gather all of the information necessary to keep appropriate records and then make the entry in your Professional Notary Records Book.

- Verify that the facts stated in the notarial certificate are accurate and complete the notarial certificate.

- Have all of the signers sign the document(s) or acknowledge having signed them previously, whichever is called for, and then perform the appropriate required oral ceremony.

- Keep the contents of the document confidential.

# COMMON ORAL CEREMONIES

As a notary, you MUST perform the appropriate oral ceremony for each notarial act.
Below are some suggested language for common notarial acts.

**ACKNOWLEDGMENT:**
*Do you hereby acknowledge that this is your signature and that you understand and have willingly signed this document?*

**AFFIRMATION:**
*Under the penalties of perjury, do you now solemnly affirm that the statements made herein are true?*

**STANDARD OATH:**
*Do you solemnly swear that the statements contained herein are true, under the penalties of perjury, so help you God?*

**OATH GIVEN TO A CREDIBLE WITNESS:**
*Do you solemnly swear that (Name of document signer) is the person named in the document; that (Name of document signer) is personally known to you; that it is your reasonable belief that the circumstances of (Name of document signer) are such that it would be unduly difficult or impossible for him or her to obtain another form of identification; that (Name of document signer) does not possess any of the acceptable forms of identification; and that you do not have a financial interest in, nor are you named in the document, so help you God?"*

**OATH FOR A SUBSCRIBING WITNESS**:
*(For use in states that allow notarization verified by a subscribing witness)*
"Do you solemnly swear that you saw (name of document signer) sign his or her name to this document and/or that he or she acknowledged to you having executed it for the purposes therein stated, so help you God?"

# Terms and Definitions

**Acknowledgment:** A formal declaration before a notary public or other authorized person by an individual signing an instrument that such execution is his or her free act and deed, and that it was signed willingly for the purpose defined in the instrument.

**Affiant:** Person who swears to an affidavit.

**Affidavit:** A written or printed statement of facts made voluntarily, verbally confirmed to be true under oath or an affirmation.

**Affirm:** To make a solemn, formal declaration of the truth of a statement or testimony, under penalty of perjury.

**Affix:** To attach or impress. Often refers to the notary seal being affixed to a document.

**Apostille:** A document used in international law that is issued by a government in accordance with the Hague Convention and that certifies that another document has been signed by a notary public.

**Attest:** To affirm to be true or genuine. Also to certify or bear witness to.

**Attorney-In-Fact:** An individual authorized to act in another's behalf by power of attorney.

**Authentication:** An act, process, or method of showing something (such as an identity, document or transaction) to be real, true, or genuine. Also the process of verification of notarial authority, usually used when a document is going to a foreign country that does not recognize or accept the authority of the Apostille.

**Certified Copy:** An exact, complete and unaltered copy of a document that is not a publicly recorded document, signed as a true copy of the original by the public official who made the copy. Note: notaries in some states are authorized to make certified copies; notaries in other states are not authorized to do so. In these states, notaries may take an affidavit from the document holder, called a certification of a copy. This affidavit states the document holder, not the notary, made a copy of the original document, and the notary completes a jurat.

**Coercion:** Forced or compelled into compliance, through fear, intimidation or threats. A notary must ensure that no coercion is used in the signing of a document. All parties must sign willingly. If the notary suspects coercion he should refuse to notarize the document.

**Commission:** The appointment as a notary, authorizing the notary to perform the official acts of that office. A commission is given by the state's authority. Also refers to the term of office. Commission term varies in length, depending on your state, from two years to lifetime appointments.

**Deed:** A document by which a person conveys (transfers) real property to another.

**Jurat:** The notary's written certificate on any sworn statement or affidavit. Document must be signed and sworn to or affirmed before the notary

**Last Will and Testament or Will:** An instrument by which an individual makes a disposition of his/her real and personal property, to take effect after his/her death.

**Oath:** A solemn affirmation of the truth of any statement, under penalty of perjury.

**Perjury:** Making a false statement under oath or affirmation. Usually punishable by fine, prison term, or both.

**Personally Known:** Having an acquaintance derived from association with an individual, which establishes the individual's identity with at least a reasonable certainty.

**Power of Attorney:** A document authorizing a person to act as another's agent or representative for a specific purpose.

**Principal:** The Person making the power of attorney.

**Reasonable Care:** That degree of care which a person of ordinary prudence and intelligence would exercise in the same or similar circumstances. Failure to exercise such care is negligence.

**Satisfactory Evidence:** Acceptable identification of an individual not personally known to the notary. Identification must have a photograph, physical description, and personal data about the individual, such as height, date of birth, and is preferably government-issued.

**Subscribe:** To sign (something, such as a document) with one's own hand in token of consent or obligation.

**Swear:** To assert as true under oath.

**Testator:** Person making a will.

**U.P.L.:** An abbreviation for the " Unlicensed Practice of Law." Notaries should proceed with extreme caution whenever asked to perform duties that appear to have legal implications.

**Venue:** The location (state and county) the notarial act actually takes place. This is typically stated in the following form: State of_____ County of_____

| Name of Signer (printed)  ① | Signer's Signature  ⑨ | Fee Charged: $  ⑧ |
|---|---|---|

Signer's FULL Address  ③ | Phone No.  ④ | Right Thumb Print (When Applicable)  ⑫

Notary Service(s) Performed  ☐ Jurat  ☐ Acknowledgment  ☐ Oath

Other(Details)  ⑤

Date Notarized:  Time:  ⑥  AM PM

**IDENTIFICATION**

Document:  Document Date:  ⑦

☐ Affidavit  ☐ Trust  ☐ Acknowledgement
☐ Mortgage/Deed  ☐ Will  ☐ Power of Attorney
☐ Auto Title  ☐ Claim  ☐ Other: _____

Notary Service Performed at:

Type:
Number:  ②
Issued By:
Expires:

Notes/Comments:  ⑬

Witness Name/Address:  ⑩ | Witness Signature:  ⑪

Known Personally:  ☐ Yes  ☐ No

**RECORD NUMBER**
**000**

# HOW TO PROPERLY COMPLETE A JOURNAL ENTRY

**1** Record the signer's full name. This can be retrieved from the ID provided.

**2** Verify the client's ID. (See note below)

**3** Record the signer's address. This can be retrieved from the ID provided. Be sure to confirm that it is their current address.

**4** Record the signer's contact phone number.

**5** Record the notary services you will be performing along with any relevant details.

**6** Record the date and time at which the notarial acts were performed.

**7** Record the types of documents being notarized and the place at which the notary acts are being performed.

**8** Record the fee being charged for the notarial services.

**9** Have the signer affix their signature to the record.

**10** Record the full name and address of any witness to the transaction(s)

**11** Have the witness affix their signature to the record.

**12** When applicable, take the thumb print of the client's right hand.

**13** Record any notes about the service you consider relevant.

An acceptable ID must be current, contain a photo and physical description of the card holder. Have the card holder's signature and a serial or ID number, such as a Driver's license or government issued ID card, Passport, or Military ID card. You should NEVER rely on Social Security cards, credit cards, or any photo ID card issued by non government entities.

It is important to record the details called for on the pages of this Professional Notary Records Book to aid you in the complete and thorough execution of your notary activities. By doing so, when you are called upon to testify regarding any of your notary transactions you will have all of the information you need available to you.

| Name of Signer (printed) | Signer's Signature | Fee Charged: $ |
|---|---|---|

**Signer's FULL Address** 1896 Union Church Rd. Thaxton, VA 24174  Phone No.

Right Thumb Print *(When Applicable)*

| Notary Service(s) Performed | ☐ Jurat | ☐ Acknowledgment | ☐ Oath |
|---|---|---|---|

Other(Details)

Date Notarized: 9/15/21   Time: 4:04 AM (PM)

**IDENTIFICATION**

| Document: | | | Document Date: |
|---|---|---|---|
| ☐ Affidavit | ☐ Trust | ☐ Acknowledgement | |
| ☐ Mortgage/Deed | ☐ Will | ☐ Power of Attorney | |
| ☐ Auto Title | ☐ Claim | ☐ Other: _____ | |

Type: DRIVER'S LICENSE
Number: TL9772H05
Issued By: 08/26/2021
Expires: 09/06/2023

Notes/Comments:

Notary Service Performed at:

| Witness Name/Address: | Witness Signature: |
|---|---|

Known Personally: ☐ Yes ☐ No

**RECORD NUMBER 1**

---

| Name of Signer (printed) Heather Anderson | Signer's Signature Heather Anderson | Fee Charged: $ |
|---|---|---|

**Signer's FULL Address**   Phone No.

Right Thumb Print *(When Applicable)*

| Notary Service(s) Performed | ☐ Jurat | ☐ Acknowledgment | ☐ Oath |
|---|---|---|---|

Other(Details) written letter was attached to notary document

Date Notarized: 6/29/22   Time: 7 AM (PM)

**IDENTIFICATION**

| Document: | | | Document Date: 6/9/22 |
|---|---|---|---|
| ☑ Affidavit | ☐ Trust | ☐ Acknowledgement | |
| ☐ Mortgage/Deed | ☐ Will | ☐ Power of Attorney | |
| ☐ Auto Title | ☐ Claim | ☐ Other: _____ | |

Type:
Number:
Issued By:
Expires:

Notes/Comments:

Notary Service Performed at: Written Letter

| Witness Name/Address: | Witness Signature: |
|---|---|

Known Personally: ☐ Yes ☐ No

**RECORD NUMBER 2**

---

| Name of Signer (printed) | Signer's Signature | Fee Charged: $ |
|---|---|---|

**Signer's FULL Address**   Phone No.

Right Thumb Print *(When Applicable)*

| Notary Service(s) Performed | ☐ Jurat | ☐ Acknowledgment | ☐ Oath |
|---|---|---|---|

Other(Details)

Date Notarized:   Time:
AM PM

**IDENTIFICATION**

| Document: | | | Document Date: |
|---|---|---|---|
| ☐ Affidavit | ☐ Trust | ☐ Acknowledgement | |
| ☐ Mortgage/Deed | ☐ Will | ☐ Power of Attorney | |
| ☐ Auto Title | ☐ Claim | ☐ Other: _____ | |

Type:
Number:
Issued By:
Expires:

Notes/Comments:

Notary Service Performed at:

| Witness Name/Address: | Witness Signature: |
|---|---|

Known Personally: ☐ Yes ☐ No

**RECORD NUMBER 3**

| Name of Signer *(printed)* | Signer's Signature | Fee Charged:$ |
|---|---|---|

| Right Thumb Print *(When Applicable)* | Signer's FULL Address | Phone No. |
|---|---|---|
| | Notary Service(s) Performed ☐Jurat ☐Acknowledgment ☐Oath <br> Other(Details) | Date Notarized: Time: <br><br> AM PM |
| Notes/Comments: | Document:                Document Date: <br> ☐ Affidavit ☐ Trust ☐ Acknowledgement <br> ☐ Mortgage/Deed ☐ Will ☐ Power of Attorney <br> ☐ Auto Title ☐ Claim ☐ Other:_____ <br> Notary Service Performed at: | **IDENTIFICATION** <br> Type: <br> Number: <br> Issued By: <br> Expires: |
| **RECORD NUMBER 4** | Witness Name/Address:        Witness Signature: | Known Personally: <br> ☐**Yes** ☐**No** |

| Name of Signer *(printed)* | Signer's Signature | Fee Charged:$ |
|---|---|---|

| Right Thumb Print *(When Applicable)* | Signer's FULL Address | Phone No. |
|---|---|---|
| | Notary Service(s) Performed ☐Jurat ☐Acknowledgment ☐Oath <br> Other(Details) | Date Notarized: Time: <br><br> AM PM |
| Notes/Comments: | Document:                Document Date: <br> ☐ Affidavit ☐ Trust ☐ Acknowledgement <br> ☐ Mortgage/Deed ☐ Will ☐ Power of Attorney <br> ☐ Auto Title ☐ Claim ☐ Other:_____ <br> Notary Service Performed at: | **IDENTIFICATION** <br> Type: <br> Number: <br> Issued By: <br> Expires: |
| **RECORD NUMBER 5** | Witness Name/Address:        Witness Signature: | Known Personally: <br> ☐**Yes** ☐**No** |

| Name of Signer *(printed)* | Signer's Signature | Fee Charged:$ |
|---|---|---|

| Right Thumb Print *(When Applicable)* | Signer's FULL Address | Phone No. |
|---|---|---|
| | Notary Service(s) Performed ☐Jurat ☐Acknowledgment ☐Oath <br> Other(Details) | Date Notarized: Time: <br><br> AM PM |
| Notes/Comments: | Document:                Document Date: <br> ☐ Affidavit ☐ Trust ☐ Acknowledgement <br> ☐ Mortgage/Deed ☐ Will ☐ Power of Attorney <br> ☐ Auto Title ☐ Claim ☐ Other:_____ <br> Notary Service Performed at: | **IDENTIFICATION** <br> Type: <br> Number: <br> Issued By: <br> Expires: |
| **RECORD NUMBER 6** | Witness Name/Address:        Witness Signature: | Known Personally: <br> ☐**Yes** ☐**No** |

| Name of Signer (printed) | Signer's Signature | Fee Charged:$ |
|---|---|---|

**Signer's FULL Address**                              Phone No.

Right Thumb Print
*(When Applicable)*

Notary Service(s) Performed    ☐ Jurat    ☐ Acknowledgment    ☐ Oath

Other(Details)

Date Notarized:          Time:

**AM  PM**

Document:                              Document Date:

☐ Affidavit        ☐ Trust        ☐ Acknowledgement
☐ Mortgage/Deed    ☐ Will         ☐ Power of Attorney
☐ Auto Title       ☐ Claim        ☐ Other: _____

Notary Service Performed at:

**IDENTIFICATION**
Type:

Number:

Issued By:

Expires:

Notes/Comments:

Witness Name/Address:                    Witness Signature:

Known Personally:
☐ Yes   ☐ No

**RECORD NUMBER
7**

---

| Name of Signer (printed) | Signer's Signature | Fee Charged:$ |
|---|---|---|

**Signer's FULL Address**                              Phone No.

Right Thumb Print
*(When Applicable)*

Notary Service(s) Performed    ☐ Jurat    ☐ Acknowledgment    ☐ Oath

Other(Details)

Date Notarized:          Time:

**AM  PM**

Document:                              Document Date:

☐ Affidavit        ☐ Trust        ☐ Acknowledgement
☐ Mortgage/Deed    ☐ Will         ☐ Power of Attorney
☐ Auto Title       ☐ Claim        ☐ Other: _____

Notary Service Performed at:

**IDENTIFICATION**
Type:

Number:

Issued By:

Expires:

Notes/Comments:

Witness Name/Address:                    Witness Signature:

Known Personally:
☐ Yes   ☐ No

**RECORD NUMBER
8**

---

| Name of Signer (printed) | Signer's Signature | Fee Charged:$ |
|---|---|---|

**Signer's FULL Address**                              Phone No.

Right Thumb Print
*(When Applicable)*

Notary Service(s) Performed    ☐ Jurat    ☐ Acknowledgment    ☐ Oath

Other(Details)

Date Notarized:          Time:

**AM  PM**

Document:                              Document Date:

☐ Affidavit        ☐ Trust        ☐ Acknowledgement
☐ Mortgage/Deed    ☐ Will         ☐ Power of Attorney
☐ Auto Title       ☐ Claim        ☐ Other: _____

Notary Service Performed at:

**IDENTIFICATION**
Type:

Number:

Issued By:

Expires:

Notes/Comments:

Witness Name/Address:                    Witness Signature:

Known Personally:
☐ Yes   ☐ No

**RECORD NUMBER
9**

| Name of Signer (printed) | Signer's Signature | Fee Charged:$ |
|---|---|---|

**Right Thumb Print** (When Applicable)

Signer's FULL Address — Phone No.

Notary Service(s) Performed ☐ Jurat ☐ Acknowledgment ☐ Oath

Other(Details)

Date Notarized: Time: AM PM

Notes/Comments:

Document: Document Date:

☐ Affidavit ☐ Trust ☐ Acknowledgement
☐ Mortgage/Deed ☐ Will ☐ Power of Attorney
☐ Auto Title ☐ Claim ☐ Other: _____

Notary Service Performed at:

**IDENTIFICATION**
Type:
Number:
Issued By:
Expires:

**RECORD NUMBER 10**

Witness Name/Address: Witness Signature:

Known Personally: ☐ Yes ☐ No

---

| Name of Signer (printed) | Signer's Signature | Fee Charged:$ |
|---|---|---|

**Right Thumb Print** (When Applicable)

Signer's FULL Address — Phone No.

Notary Service(s) Performed ☐ Jurat ☐ Acknowledgment ☐ Oath

Other(Details)

Date Notarized: Time: AM PM

Notes/Comments:

Document: Document Date:

☐ Affidavit ☐ Trust ☐ Acknowledgement
☐ Mortgage/Deed ☐ Will ☐ Power of Attorney
☐ Auto Title ☐ Claim ☐ Other: _____

Notary Service Performed at:

**IDENTIFICATION**
Type:
Number:
Issued By:
Expires:

**RECORD NUMBER 11**

Witness Name/Address: Witness Signature:

Known Personally: ☐ Yes ☐ No

---

| Name of Signer (printed) | Signer's Signature | Fee Charged:$ |
|---|---|---|

**Right Thumb Print** (When Applicable)

Signer's FULL Address — Phone No.

Notary Service(s) Performed ☐ Jurat ☐ Acknowledgment ☐ Oath

Other(Details)

Date Notarized: Time: AM PM

Notes/Comments:

Document: Document Date:

☐ Affidavit ☐ Trust ☐ Acknowledgement
☐ Mortgage/Deed ☐ Will ☐ Power of Attorney
☐ Auto Title ☐ Claim ☐ Other: _____

Notary Service Performed at:

**IDENTIFICATION**
Type:
Number:
Issued By:
Expires:

**RECORD NUMBER 12**

Witness Name/Address: Witness Signature:

Known Personally: ☐ Yes ☐ No

| Name of Signer (printed) | Signer's Signature | Fee Charged: $ |
|---|---|---|

Signer's FULL Address        Phone No.    | Right Thumb Print *(When Applicable)*

Notary Service(s) Performed   ☐ Jurat   ☐ Acknowledgment   ☐ Oath

Other(Details)

Date Notarized:    Time:    **AM PM**

Document:        Document Date:

☐ Affidavit    ☐ Trust    ☐ Acknowledgement
☐ Mortgage/Deed    ☐ Will    ☐ Power of Attorney
☐ Auto Title    ☐ Claim    ☐ Other: _____

Notary Service Performed at:

**IDENTIFICATION**
Type:
Number:
Issued By:
Expires:

Notes/Comments:

Witness Name/Address:      Witness Signature:

Known Personally:   ☐ Yes   ☐ No

**RECORD NUMBER 13**

---

| Name of Signer (printed) | Signer's Signature | Fee Charged: $ |
|---|---|---|

Signer's FULL Address        Phone No.    | Right Thumb Print *(When Applicable)*

Notary Service(s) Performed   ☐ Jurat   ☐ Acknowledgment   ☐ Oath

Other(Details)

Date Notarized:    Time:    **AM PM**

Document:        Document Date:

☐ Affidavit    ☐ Trust    ☐ Acknowledgement
☐ Mortgage/Deed    ☐ Will    ☐ Power of Attorney
☐ Auto Title    ☐ Claim    ☐ Other: _____

Notary Service Performed at:

**IDENTIFICATION**
Type:
Number:
Issued By:
Expires:

Notes/Comments:

Witness Name/Address:      Witness Signature:

Known Personally:   ☐ Yes   ☐ No

**RECORD NUMBER 14**

---

| Name of Signer (printed) | Signer's Signature | Fee Charged: $ |
|---|---|---|

Signer's FULL Address        Phone No.    | Right Thumb Print *(When Applicable)*

Notary Service(s) Performed   ☐ Jurat   ☐ Acknowledgment   ☐ Oath

Other(Details)

Date Notarized:    Time:    **AM PM**

Document:        Document Date:

☐ Affidavit    ☐ Trust    ☐ Acknowledgement
☐ Mortgage/Deed    ☐ Will    ☐ Power of Attorney
☐ Auto Title    ☐ Claim    ☐ Other: _____

Notary Service Performed at:

**IDENTIFICATION**
Type:
Number:
Issued By:
Expires:

Notes/Comments:

Witness Name/Address:      Witness Signature:

Known Personally:   ☐ Yes   ☐ No

**RECORD NUMBER 15**

| Name of Signer (printed) | Signer's Signature | Fee Charged:$ |
|---|---|---|

| Right Thumb Print (When Applicable) | Signer's FULL Address | Phone No. |
|---|---|---|
| | Notary Service(s) Performed ☐Jurat ☐Acknowledgment ☐Oath | Date Notarized: Time: |
| | Other(Details) | AM PM |
| Notes/Comments: | Document: Document Date: | **IDENTIFICATION** Type: |
| | ☐ Affidavit ☐ Trust ☐ Acknowledgement | Number: |
| | ☐ Mortgage/Deed ☐ Will ☐ Power of Attorney | Issued By: |
| | ☐ Auto Title ☐ Claim ☐ Other:_____ | Expires: |
| | Notary Service Performed at: | |
| **RECORD NUMBER 16** | Witness Name/Address: Witness Signature: | Known Personally: ☐Yes ☐No |

| Name of Signer (printed) | Signer's Signature | Fee Charged:$ |
|---|---|---|

| Right Thumb Print (When Applicable) | Signer's FULL Address | Phone No. |
|---|---|---|
| | Notary Service(s) Performed ☐Jurat ☐Acknowledgment ☐Oath | Date Notarized: Time: |
| | Other(Details) | AM PM |
| Notes/Comments: | Document: Document Date: | **IDENTIFICATION** Type: |
| | ☐ Affidavit ☐ Trust ☐ Acknowledgement | Number: |
| | ☐ Mortgage/Deed ☐ Will ☐ Power of Attorney | Issued By: |
| | ☐ Auto Title ☐ Claim ☐ Other:_____ | Expires: |
| | Notary Service Performed at: | |
| **RECORD NUMBER 17** | Witness Name/Address: Witness Signature: | Known Personally: ☐Yes ☐No |

| Name of Signer (printed) | Signer's Signature | Fee Charged:$ |
|---|---|---|

| Right Thumb Print (When Applicable) | Signer's FULL Address | Phone No. |
|---|---|---|
| | Notary Service(s) Performed ☐Jurat ☐Acknowledgment ☐Oath | Date Notarized: Time: |
| | Other(Details) | AM PM |
| Notes/Comments: | Document: Document Date: | **IDENTIFICATION** Type: |
| | ☐ Affidavit ☐ Trust ☐ Acknowledgement | Number: |
| | ☐ Mortgage/Deed ☐ Will ☐ Power of Attorney | Issued By: |
| | ☐ Auto Title ☐ Claim ☐ Other:_____ | Expires: |
| | Notary Service Performed at: | |
| **RECORD NUMBER 18** | Witness Name/Address: Witness Signature: | Known Personally: ☐Yes ☐No |

| Name of Signer *(printed)* | Signer's Signature | Fee Charged:$ |
|---|---|---|

**Signer's FULL Address**  Phone No.  Right Thumb Print *(When Applicable)*

Notary Service(s) Performed  ☐ Jurat  ☐ Acknowledgment  ☐ Oath

Other(Details)

Date Notarized:  Time:

AM PM

**Document:**  Document Date:

☐ Affidavit  ☐ Trust  ☐ Acknowledgement

☐ Mortgage/Deed  ☐ Will  ☐ Power of Attorney

☐ Auto Title  ☐ Claim  ☐ Other: _____

Notary Service Performed at:

**IDENTIFICATION**

Type:

Number:

Issued By:

Expires:

Notes/Comments:

Witness Name/Address:  Witness Signature:

Known Personally:  ☐ Yes  ☐ No

**RECORD NUMBER 19**

---

| Name of Signer *(printed)* | Signer's Signature | Fee Charged:$ |
|---|---|---|

**Signer's FULL Address**  Phone No.  Right Thumb Print *(When Applicable)*

Notary Service(s) Performed  ☐ Jurat  ☐ Acknowledgment  ☐ Oath

Other(Details)

Date Notarized:  Time:

AM PM

**Document:**  Document Date:

☐ Affidavit  ☐ Trust  ☐ Acknowledgement

☐ Mortgage/Deed  ☐ Will  ☐ Power of Attorney

☐ Auto Title  ☐ Claim  ☐ Other: _____

Notary Service Performed at:

**IDENTIFICATION**

Type:

Number:

Issued By:

Expires:

Notes/Comments:

Witness Name/Address:  Witness Signature:

Known Personally:  ☐ Yes  ☐ No

**RECORD NUMBER 20**

---

| Name of Signer *(printed)* | Signer's Signature | Fee Charged:$ |
|---|---|---|

**Signer's FULL Address**  Phone No.  Right Thumb Print *(When Applicable)*

Notary Service(s) Performed  ☐ Jurat  ☐ Acknowledgment  ☐ Oath

Other(Details)

Date Notarized:  Time:

AM PM

**Document:**  Document Date:

☐ Affidavit  ☐ Trust  ☐ Acknowledgement

☐ Mortgage/Deed  ☐ Will  ☐ Power of Attorney

☐ Auto Title  ☐ Claim  ☐ Other: _____

Notary Service Performed at:

**IDENTIFICATION**

Type:

Number:

Issued By:

Expires:

Notes/Comments:

Witness Name/Address:  Witness Signature:

Known Personally:  ☐ Yes  ☐ No

**RECORD NUMBER 21**

| Name of Signer (printed) | Signer's Signature | Fee Charged:$ |
|---|---|---|

| Right Thumb Print (When Applicable) | Signer's FULL Address | | Phone No. |
|---|---|---|---|

**Notary Service(s) Performed** ☐ Jurat ☐ Acknowledgment ☐ Oath

Other(Details)

| Date Notarized: | Time: |
|---|---|
| | AM PM |

**IDENTIFICATION**

| Notes/Comments: | Document: | Document Date: |
|---|---|---|

☐ Affidavit ☐ Trust ☐ Acknowledgement
☐ Mortgage/Deed ☐ Will ☐ Power of Attorney
☐ Auto Title ☐ Claim ☐ Other: _____

Notary Service Performed at:

Type:

Number:

Issued By:

Expires:

| **RECORD NUMBER 22** | Witness Name/Address: | Witness Signature: | Known Personally: ☐ Yes ☐ No |
|---|---|---|---|

---

| Name of Signer (printed) | Signer's Signature | Fee Charged:$ |
|---|---|---|

| Right Thumb Print (When Applicable) | Signer's FULL Address | | Phone No. |
|---|---|---|---|

**Notary Service(s) Performed** ☐ Jurat ☐ Acknowledgment ☐ Oath

Other(Details)

| Date Notarized: | Time: |
|---|---|
| | AM PM |

**IDENTIFICATION**

| Notes/Comments: | Document: | Document Date: |
|---|---|---|

☐ Affidavit ☐ Trust ☐ Acknowledgement
☐ Mortgage/Deed ☐ Will ☐ Power of Attorney
☐ Auto Title ☐ Claim ☐ Other: _____

Notary Service Performed at:

Type:

Number:

Issued By:

Expires:

| **RECORD NUMBER 23** | Witness Name/Address: | Witness Signature: | Known Personally: ☐ Yes ☐ No |
|---|---|---|---|

---

| Name of Signer (printed) | Signer's Signature | Fee Charged:$ |
|---|---|---|

| Right Thumb Print (When Applicable) | Signer's FULL Address | | Phone No. |
|---|---|---|---|

**Notary Service(s) Performed** ☐ Jurat ☐ Acknowledgment ☐ Oath

Other(Details)

| Date Notarized: | Time: |
|---|---|
| | AM PM |

**IDENTIFICATION**

| Notes/Comments: | Document: | Document Date: |
|---|---|---|

☐ Affidavit ☐ Trust ☐ Acknowledgement
☐ Mortgage/Deed ☐ Will ☐ Power of Attorney
☐ Auto Title ☐ Claim ☐ Other: _____

Notary Service Performed at:

Type:

Number:

Issued By:

Expires:

| **RECORD NUMBER 24** | Witness Name/Address: | Witness Signature: | Known Personally: ☐ Yes ☐ No |
|---|---|---|---|

| Name of Signer *(printed)* | Signer's Signature | Fee Charged:$ |
|---|---|---|

**Signer's FULL Address** — Phone No. — Right Thumb Print *(When Applicable)*

Notary Service(s) Performed ☐Jurat ☐Acknowledgment ☐Oath — Date Notarized: — Time: — AM PM

Other(Details)

Document: — Document Date:

**IDENTIFICATION**
Type:
Number:
Issued By:
Expires:

☐ Affidavit ☐ Trust ☐ Acknowledgement
☐ Mortgage/Deed ☐ Will ☐ Power of Attorney
☐ Auto Title ☐ Claim ☐ Other: _____

Notary Service Performed at:

Notes/Comments:

Witness Name/Address: — Witness Signature:

Known Personally: ☐ Yes ☐ No

**RECORD NUMBER 25**

---

| Name of Signer *(printed)* | Signer's Signature | Fee Charged:$ |
|---|---|---|

**Signer's FULL Address** — Phone No. — Right Thumb Print *(When Applicable)*

Notary Service(s) Performed ☐Jurat ☐Acknowledgment ☐Oath — Date Notarized: — Time: — AM PM

Other(Details)

Document: — Document Date:

**IDENTIFICATION**
Type:
Number:
Issued By:
Expires:

☐ Affidavit ☐ Trust ☐ Acknowledgement
☐ Mortgage/Deed ☐ Will ☐ Power of Attorney
☐ Auto Title ☐ Claim ☐ Other: _____

Notary Service Performed at:

Notes/Comments:

Witness Name/Address: — Witness Signature:

Known Personally: ☐ Yes ☐ No

**RECORD NUMBER 26**

---

| Name of Signer *(printed)* | Signer's Signature | Fee Charged:$ |
|---|---|---|

**Signer's FULL Address** — Phone No. — Right Thumb Print *(When Applicable)*

Notary Service(s) Performed ☐Jurat ☐Acknowledgment ☐Oath — Date Notarized: — Time: — AM PM

Other(Details)

Document: — Document Date:

**IDENTIFICATION**
Type:
Number:
Issued By:
Expires:

☐ Affidavit ☐ Trust ☐ Acknowledgement
☐ Mortgage/Deed ☐ Will ☐ Power of Attorney
☐ Auto Title ☐ Claim ☐ Other: _____

Notary Service Performed at:

Notes/Comments:

Witness Name/Address: — Witness Signature:

Known Personally: ☐ Yes ☐ No

**RECORD NUMBER 27**

## RECORD NUMBER 28

| Name of Signer (printed) | Signer's Signature | Fee Charged:$ |
|---|---|---|

**Right Thumb Print** (When Applicable)

Signer's FULL Address — Phone No.

Notary Service(s) Performed ☐Jurat ☐Acknowledgment ☐Oath

Other(Details)

Date Notarized: Time: AM PM

Notes/Comments:

Document: Document Date:

- ☐ Affidavit
- ☐ Mortgage/Deed
- ☐ Auto Title
- ☐ Trust
- ☐ Will
- ☐ Claim
- ☐ Acknowledgement
- ☐ Power of Attorney
- ☐ Other: _____

Notary Service Performed at:

**IDENTIFICATION**
Type:
Number:
Issued By:
Expires:

Witness Name/Address: Witness Signature:

Known Personally: ☐Yes ☐No

---

## RECORD NUMBER 29

| Name of Signer (printed) | Signer's Signature | Fee Charged:$ |
|---|---|---|

**Right Thumb Print** (When Applicable)

Signer's FULL Address — Phone No.

Notary Service(s) Performed ☐Jurat ☐Acknowledgment ☐Oath

Other(Details)

Date Notarized: Time: AM PM

Notes/Comments:

Document: Document Date:

- ☐ Affidavit
- ☐ Mortgage/Deed
- ☐ Auto Title
- ☐ Trust
- ☐ Will
- ☐ Claim
- ☐ Acknowledgement
- ☐ Power of Attorney
- ☐ Other: _____

Notary Service Performed at:

**IDENTIFICATION**
Type:
Number:
Issued By:
Expires:

Witness Name/Address: Witness Signature:

Known Personally: ☐Yes ☐No

---

## RECORD NUMBER 30

| Name of Signer (printed) | Signer's Signature | Fee Charged:$ |
|---|---|---|

**Right Thumb Print** (When Applicable)

Signer's FULL Address — Phone No.

Notary Service(s) Performed ☐Jurat ☐Acknowledgment ☐Oath

Other(Details)

Date Notarized: Time: AM PM

Notes/Comments:

Document: Document Date:

- ☐ Affidavit
- ☐ Mortgage/Deed
- ☐ Auto Title
- ☐ Trust
- ☐ Will
- ☐ Claim
- ☐ Acknowledgement
- ☐ Power of Attorney
- ☐ Other: _____

Notary Service Performed at:

**IDENTIFICATION**
Type:
Number:
Issued By:
Expires:

Witness Name/Address: Witness Signature:

Known Personally: ☐Yes ☐No

Name of Signer *(printed)* | Signer's Signature | Fee Charged: $

Signer's FULL Address | Phone No. | Right Thumb Print *(When Applicable)*

Notary Service(s) Performed ☐ Jurat ☐ Acknowledgment ☐ Oath | Date Notarized: Time:

Other(Details) | AM PM

**IDENTIFICATION**
Type:

Document: | Document Date: | Number:

☐ Affidavit ☐ Trust ☐ Acknowledgement | Issued By:
☐ Mortgage/Deed ☐ Will ☐ Power of Attorney
☐ Auto Title ☐ Claim ☐ Other: _____ | Expires:

Notary Service Performed at:

Notes/Comments:

Witness Name/Address: | Witness Signature: | Known Personally: ☐ Yes ☐ No | **RECORD NUMBER 31**

---

Name of Signer *(printed)* | Signer's Signature | Fee Charged: $

Signer's FULL Address | Phone No. | Right Thumb Print *(When Applicable)*

Notary Service(s) Performed ☐ Jurat ☐ Acknowledgment ☐ Oath | Date Notarized: Time:

Other(Details) | AM PM

**IDENTIFICATION**
Type:

Document: | Document Date: | Number:

☐ Affidavit ☐ Trust ☐ Acknowledgement | Issued By:
☐ Mortgage/Deed ☐ Will ☐ Power of Attorney
☐ Auto Title ☐ Claim ☐ Other: _____ | Expires:

Notary Service Performed at:

Notes/Comments:

Witness Name/Address: | Witness Signature: | Known Personally: ☐ Yes ☐ No | **RECORD NUMBER 32**

---

Name of Signer *(printed)* | Signer's Signature | Fee Charged: $

Signer's FULL Address | Phone No. | Right Thumb Print *(When Applicable)*

Notary Service(s) Performed ☐ Jurat ☐ Acknowledgment ☐ Oath | Date Notarized: Time:

Other(Details) | AM PM

**IDENTIFICATION**
Type:

Document: | Document Date: | Number:

☐ Affidavit ☐ Trust ☐ Acknowledgement | Issued By:
☐ Mortgage/Deed ☐ Will ☐ Power of Attorney
☐ Auto Title ☐ Claim ☐ Other: _____ | Expires:

Notary Service Performed at:

Notes/Comments:

Witness Name/Address: | Witness Signature: | Known Personally: ☐ Yes ☐ No | **RECORD NUMBER 33**

| Name of Signer (printed) | Signer's Signature | Fee Charged: $ |
|---|---|---|

| Right Thumb Print (When Applicable) | Signer's FULL Address | Phone No. |
|---|---|---|

**Notary Service(s) Performed** ☐ Jurat ☐ Acknowledgment ☐ Oath

Other(Details)

| | Date Notarized: | Time: |
|---|---|---|
| | | AM  PM |

**IDENTIFICATION**

Document: Document Date:

Type:

☐ Affidavit ☐ Trust ☐ Acknowledgement

Number:

☐ Mortgage/Deed ☐ Will ☐ Power of Attorney

Issued By:

☐ Auto Title ☐ Claim ☐ Other: _____

Notary Service Performed at:

Expires:

Notes/Comments:

Witness Name/Address: Witness Signature:

Known Personally:

**RECORD NUMBER 34**

☐ Yes ☐ No

---

| Name of Signer (printed) | Signer's Signature | Fee Charged: $ |
|---|---|---|

| Right Thumb Print (When Applicable) | Signer's FULL Address | Phone No. |
|---|---|---|

**Notary Service(s) Performed** ☐ Jurat ☐ Acknowledgment ☐ Oath

Other(Details)

| | Date Notarized: | Time: |
|---|---|---|
| | | AM  PM |

**IDENTIFICATION**

Document: Document Date:

Type:

☐ Affidavit ☐ Trust ☐ Acknowledgement

Number:

☐ Mortgage/Deed ☐ Will ☐ Power of Attorney

Issued By:

☐ Auto Title ☐ Claim ☐ Other: _____

Notary Service Performed at:

Expires:

Notes/Comments:

Witness Name/Address: Witness Signature:

Known Personally:

**RECORD NUMBER 35**

☐ Yes ☐ No

---

| Name of Signer (printed) | Signer's Signature | Fee Charged: $ |
|---|---|---|

| Right Thumb Print (When Applicable) | Signer's FULL Address | Phone No. |
|---|---|---|

**Notary Service(s) Performed** ☐ Jurat ☐ Acknowledgment ☐ Oath

Other(Details)

| | Date Notarized: | Time: |
|---|---|---|
| | | AM  PM |

**IDENTIFICATION**

Document: Document Date:

Type:

☐ Affidavit ☐ Trust ☐ Acknowledgement

Number:

☐ Mortgage/Deed ☐ Will ☐ Power of Attorney

Issued By:

☐ Auto Title ☐ Claim ☐ Other: _____

Notary Service Performed at:

Expires:

Notes/Comments:

Witness Name/Address: Witness Signature:

Known Personally:

**RECORD NUMBER 36**

☐ Yes ☐ No

| Name of Signer (printed) | Signer's Signature | Fee Charged:$ |
|---|---|---|

**Signer's FULL Address**      Phone No.     Right Thumb Print *(When Applicable)*

Notary Service(s) Performed   ☐ Jurat   ☐ Acknowledgment   ☐ Oath    Date Notarized:    Time:

Other(Details)       **AM PM**

**IDENTIFICATION**

Document:         Document Date:    Type:      Notes/Comments:

☐ Affidavit    ☐ Trust    ☐ Acknowledgement    Number:

☐ Mortgage/Deed    ☐ Will    ☐ Power of Attorney    Issued By:

☐ Auto Title    ☐ Claim    ☐ Other: _____    Expires:

Notary Service Performed at:

Witness Name/Address:     Witness Signature:     Known Personally: ☐ Yes ☐ No    **RECORD NUMBER 37**

---

| Name of Signer (printed) | Signer's Signature | Fee Charged:$ |
|---|---|---|

**Signer's FULL Address**      Phone No.     Right Thumb Print *(When Applicable)*

Notary Service(s) Performed   ☐ Jurat   ☐ Acknowledgment   ☐ Oath    Date Notarized:    Time:

Other(Details)       **AM PM**

**IDENTIFICATION**

Document:         Document Date:    Type:      Notes/Comments:

☐ Affidavit    ☐ Trust    ☐ Acknowledgement    Number:

☐ Mortgage/Deed    ☐ Will    ☐ Power of Attorney    Issued By:

☐ Auto Title    ☐ Claim    ☐ Other: _____    Expires:

Notary Service Performed at:

Witness Name/Address:     Witness Signature:     Known Personally: ☐ Yes ☐ No    **RECORD NUMBER 38**

---

| Name of Signer (printed) | Signer's Signature | Fee Charged:$ |
|---|---|---|

**Signer's FULL Address**      Phone No.     Right Thumb Print *(When Applicable)*

Notary Service(s) Performed   ☐ Jurat   ☐ Acknowledgment   ☐ Oath    Date Notarized:    Time:

Other(Details)       **AM PM**

**IDENTIFICATION**

Document:         Document Date:    Type:      Notes/Comments:

☐ Affidavit    ☐ Trust    ☐ Acknowledgement    Number:

☐ Mortgage/Deed    ☐ Will    ☐ Power of Attorney    Issued By:

☐ Auto Title    ☐ Claim    ☐ Other: _____    Expires:

Notary Service Performed at:

Witness Name/Address:     Witness Signature:     Known Personally: ☐ Yes ☐ No    **RECORD NUMBER 39**

| Name of Signer (*printed*) | Signer's Signature | Fee Charged:$ |
|---|---|---|

| Right Thumb Print (*When Applicable*) | Signer's FULL Address | Phone No. |
|---|---|---|

**Notary Service(s) Performed** ☐Jurat ☐Acknowledgment ☐Oath

Other(Details)

**Date Notarized:** **Time:**

**AM PM**

**IDENTIFICATION**

Type:

Number:

Issued By:

Expires:

Document: Document Date:

☐ Affidavit ☐ Trust ☐ Acknowledgement
☐ Mortgage/Deed ☐ Will ☐ Power of Attorney
☐ Auto Title ☐ Claim ☐ Other: _____

Notary Service Performed at:

Notes/Comments:

Witness Name/Address: Witness Signature:

**Known Personally:** ☐Yes ☐No

**RECORD NUMBER 40**

---

| Name of Signer (*printed*) | Signer's Signature | Fee Charged:$ |
|---|---|---|

| Right Thumb Print (*When Applicable*) | Signer's FULL Address | Phone No. |
|---|---|---|

**Notary Service(s) Performed** ☐Jurat ☐Acknowledgment ☐Oath

Other(Details)

**Date Notarized:** **Time:**

**AM PM**

**IDENTIFICATION**

Type:

Number:

Issued By:

Expires:

Document: Document Date:

☐ Affidavit ☐ Trust ☐ Acknowledgement
☐ Mortgage/Deed ☐ Will ☐ Power of Attorney
☐ Auto Title ☐ Claim ☐ Other: _____

Notary Service Performed at:

Notes/Comments:

Witness Name/Address: Witness Signature:

**Known Personally:** ☐Yes ☐No

**RECORD NUMBER 41**

---

| Name of Signer (*printed*) | Signer's Signature | Fee Charged:$ |
|---|---|---|

| Right Thumb Print (*When Applicable*) | Signer's FULL Address | Phone No. |
|---|---|---|

**Notary Service(s) Performed** ☐Jurat ☐Acknowledgment ☐Oath

Other(Details)

**Date Notarized:** **Time:**

**AM PM**

**IDENTIFICATION**

Type:

Number:

Issued By:

Expires:

Document: Document Date:

☐ Affidavit ☐ Trust ☐ Acknowledgement
☐ Mortgage/Deed ☐ Will ☐ Power of Attorney
☐ Auto Title ☐ Claim ☐ Other: _____

Notary Service Performed at:

Notes/Comments:

Witness Name/Address: Witness Signature:

**Known Personally:** ☐Yes ☐No

**RECORD NUMBER 42**

| Name of Signer (printed) | Signer's Signature | Fee Charged:$ |
|---|---|---|

Signer's FULL Address                                     Phone No.

| | Right Thumb Print (When Applicable) |
|---|---|

Notary Service(s) Performed   ☐ Jurat   ☐ Acknowledgment   ☐ Oath

Other(Details)

Date Notarized:          Time:

AM  PM

**Document:**                                  Document Date:

**IDENTIFICATION**

Type:

☐ Affidavit        ☐ Trust        ☐ Acknowledgement

☐ Mortgage/Deed    ☐ Will         ☐ Power of Attorney

☐ Auto Title       ☐ Claim        ☐ Other: _____

Notary Service Performed at:

Number:

Issued By:

Expires:

Notes/Comments:

Witness Name/Address:                   Witness Signature:

Known Personally:

☐ Yes   ☐ No

**RECORD NUMBER**
**43**

---

| Name of Signer (printed) | Signer's Signature | Fee Charged:$ |
|---|---|---|

Signer's FULL Address                                     Phone No.

| | Right Thumb Print (When Applicable) |
|---|---|

Notary Service(s) Performed   ☐ Jurat   ☐ Acknowledgment   ☐ Oath

Other(Details)

Date Notarized:          Time:

AM  PM

**Document:**                                  Document Date:

**IDENTIFICATION**

Type:

☐ Affidavit        ☐ Trust        ☐ Acknowledgement

☐ Mortgage/Deed    ☐ Will         ☐ Power of Attorney

☐ Auto Title       ☐ Claim        ☐ Other: _____

Notary Service Performed at:

Number:

Issued By:

Expires:

Notes/Comments:

Witness Name/Address:                   Witness Signature:

Known Personally:

☐ Yes   ☐ No

**RECORD NUMBER**
**44**

---

| Name of Signer (printed) | Signer's Signature | Fee Charged:$ |
|---|---|---|

Signer's FULL Address                                     Phone No.

| | Right Thumb Print (When Applicable) |
|---|---|

Notary Service(s) Performed   ☐ Jurat   ☐ Acknowledgment   ☐ Oath

Other(Details)

Date Notarized:          Time:

AM  PM

**Document:**                                  Document Date:

**IDENTIFICATION**

Type:

☐ Affidavit        ☐ Trust        ☐ Acknowledgement

☐ Mortgage/Deed    ☐ Will         ☐ Power of Attorney

☐ Auto Title       ☐ Claim        ☐ Other: _____

Notary Service Performed at:

Number:

Issued By:

Expires:

Notes/Comments:

Witness Name/Address:                   Witness Signature:

Known Personally:

☐ Yes   ☐ No

**RECORD NUMBER**
**45**

| Name of Signer (printed) | Signer's Signature | Fee Charged: $ |
| --- | --- | --- |

**Right Thumb Print** (When Applicable)

Signer's FULL Address

Phone No.

Notary Service(s) Performed  ☐ Jurat  ☐ Acknowledgment  ☐ Oath

Other(Details)

Date Notarized:  Time:

AM  PM

**IDENTIFICATION**

Notes/Comments:

Document:  Document Date:

☐ Affidavit  ☐ Trust  ☐ Acknowledgement
☐ Mortgage/Deed  ☐ Will  ☐ Power of Attorney
☐ Auto Title  ☐ Claim  ☐ Other: _____

Notary Service Performed at:

Type:

Number:

Issued By:

Expires:

**RECORD NUMBER 46**

Witness Name/Address:  Witness Signature:

Known Personally:

☐ Yes  ☐ No

---

| Name of Signer (printed) | Signer's Signature | Fee Charged: $ |
| --- | --- | --- |

**Right Thumb Print** (When Applicable)

Signer's FULL Address

Phone No.

Notary Service(s) Performed  ☐ Jurat  ☐ Acknowledgment  ☐ Oath

Other(Details)

Date Notarized:  Time:

AM  PM

**IDENTIFICATION**

Notes/Comments:

Document:  Document Date:

☐ Affidavit  ☐ Trust  ☐ Acknowledgement
☐ Mortgage/Deed  ☐ Will  ☐ Power of Attorney
☐ Auto Title  ☐ Claim  ☐ Other: _____

Notary Service Performed at:

Type:

Number:

Issued By:

Expires:

**RECORD NUMBER 47**

Witness Name/Address:  Witness Signature:

Known Personally:

☐ Yes  ☐ No

---

| Name of Signer (printed) | Signer's Signature | Fee Charged: $ |
| --- | --- | --- |

**Right Thumb Print** (When Applicable)

Signer's FULL Address

Phone No.

Notary Service(s) Performed  ☐ Jurat  ☐ Acknowledgment  ☐ Oath

Other(Details)

Date Notarized:  Time:

AM  PM

**IDENTIFICATION**

Notes/Comments:

Document:  Document Date:

☐ Affidavit  ☐ Trust  ☐ Acknowledgement
☐ Mortgage/Deed  ☐ Will  ☐ Power of Attorney
☐ Auto Title  ☐ Claim  ☐ Other: _____

Notary Service Performed at:

Type:

Number:

Issued By:

Expires:

**RECORD NUMBER 48**

Witness Name/Address:  Witness Signature:

Known Personally:

☐ Yes  ☐ No

| Name of Signer (printed) | Signer's Signature | Fee Charged: $ |
|---|---|---|

Signer's FULL Address  Phone No.

Right Thumb Print
*(When Applicable)*

Notary Service(s) Performed  ☐ Jurat  ☐ Acknowledgment  ☐ Oath

Other(Details)

Date Notarized:  Time:

AM  PM

Document:  Document Date:

**IDENTIFICATION**

Type:

☐ Affidavit  ☐ Trust  ☐ Acknowledgement

☐ Mortgage/Deed  ☐ Will  ☐ Power of Attorney

☐ Auto Title  ☐ Claim  ☐ Other: _____

Number:

Issued By:

Notary Service Performed at:

Expires:

Notes/Comments:

Witness Name/Address:  Witness Signature:

Known Personally:

☐ Yes  ☐ No

**RECORD NUMBER
49**

---

| Name of Signer (printed) | Signer's Signature | Fee Charged: $ |
|---|---|---|

Signer's FULL Address  Phone No.

Right Thumb Print
*(When Applicable)*

Notary Service(s) Performed  ☐ Jurat  ☐ Acknowledgment  ☐ Oath

Other(Details)

Date Notarized:  Time:

AM  PM

Document:  Document Date:

**IDENTIFICATION**

Type:

☐ Affidavit  ☐ Trust  ☐ Acknowledgement

☐ Mortgage/Deed  ☐ Will  ☐ Power of Attorney

☐ Auto Title  ☐ Claim  ☐ Other: _____

Number:

Issued By:

Notary Service Performed at:

Expires:

Notes/Comments:

Witness Name/Address:  Witness Signature:

Known Personally:

☐ Yes  ☐ No

**RECORD NUMBER
50**

---

| Name of Signer (printed) | Signer's Signature | Fee Charged: $ |
|---|---|---|

Signer's FULL Address  Phone No.

Right Thumb Print
*(When Applicable)*

Notary Service(s) Performed  ☐ Jurat  ☐ Acknowledgment  ☐ Oath

Other(Details)

Date Notarized:  Time:

AM  PM

Document:  Document Date:

**IDENTIFICATION**

Type:

☐ Affidavit  ☐ Trust  ☐ Acknowledgement

☐ Mortgage/Deed  ☐ Will  ☐ Power of Attorney

☐ Auto Title  ☐ Claim  ☐ Other: _____

Number:

Issued By:

Notary Service Performed at:

Expires:

Notes/Comments:

Witness Name/Address:  Witness Signature:

Known Personally:

☐ Yes  ☐ No

**RECORD NUMBER
51**

| Name of Signer (printed) | Signer's Signature | Fee Charged:$ |
| --- | --- | --- |

| Right Thumb Print (When Applicable) | Signer's FULL Address | Phone No. |
| --- | --- | --- |
| | Notary Service(s) Performed  ☐ Jurat  ☐ Acknowledgment  ☐ Oath  Other(Details) | Date Notarized:  Time:  AM  PM |
| Notes/Comments: | Document:  Document Date:  ☐ Affidavit  ☐ Trust  ☐ Acknowledgement  ☐ Mortgage/Deed  ☐ Will  ☐ Power of Attorney  ☐ Auto Title  ☐ Claim  ☐ Other: _____  Notary Service Performed at: | **IDENTIFICATION**  Type:  Number:  Issued By:  Expires: |
| **RECORD NUMBER 52** | Witness Name/Address:  Witness Signature: | Known Personally:  ☐ Yes  ☐ No |

| Name of Signer (printed) | Signer's Signature | Fee Charged:$ |
| --- | --- | --- |

| Right Thumb Print (When Applicable) | Signer's FULL Address | Phone No. |
| --- | --- | --- |
| | Notary Service(s) Performed  ☐ Jurat  ☐ Acknowledgment  ☐ Oath  Other(Details) | Date Notarized:  Time:  AM  PM |
| Notes/Comments: | Document:  Document Date:  ☐ Affidavit  ☐ Trust  ☐ Acknowledgement  ☐ Mortgage/Deed  ☐ Will  ☐ Power of Attorney  ☐ Auto Title  ☐ Claim  ☐ Other: _____  Notary Service Performed at: | **IDENTIFICATION**  Type:  Number:  Issued By:  Expires: |
| **RECORD NUMBER 53** | Witness Name/Address:  Witness Signature: | Known Personally:  ☐ Yes  ☐ No |

| Name of Signer (printed) | Signer's Signature | Fee Charged:$ |
| --- | --- | --- |

| Right Thumb Print (When Applicable) | Signer's FULL Address | Phone No. |
| --- | --- | --- |
| | Notary Service(s) Performed  ☐ Jurat  ☐ Acknowledgment  ☐ Oath  Other(Details) | Date Notarized:  Time:  AM  PM |
| Notes/Comments: | Document:  Document Date:  ☐ Affidavit  ☐ Trust  ☐ Acknowledgement  ☐ Mortgage/Deed  ☐ Will  ☐ Power of Attorney  ☐ Auto Title  ☐ Claim  ☐ Other: _____  Notary Service Performed at: | **IDENTIFICATION**  Type:  Number:  Issued By:  Expires: |
| **RECORD NUMBER 54** | Witness Name/Address:  Witness Signature: | Known Personally:  ☐ Yes  ☐ No |

| Name of Signer *(printed)* | Signer's Signature | Fee Charged:$ |
| --- | --- | --- |

**Signer's FULL Address**  Phone No.

**Right Thumb Print**
*(When Applicable)*

Notary Service(s) Performed ☐ Jurat ☐ Acknowledgment ☐ Oath

Other(Details)

Date Notarized:  Time:

AM PM

Document:  Document Date:

**IDENTIFICATION**

Type:

☐ Affidavit ☐ Trust ☐ Acknowledgement

☐ Mortgage/Deed ☐ Will ☐ Power of Attorney

☐ Auto Title ☐ Claim ☐ Other: _____

Notary Service Performed at:

Number:

Issued By:

Expires:

Notes/Comments:

Witness Name/Address:  Witness Signature:

Known Personally:

☐ Yes ☐ No

**RECORD NUMBER**
**55**

---

| Name of Signer *(printed)* | Signer's Signature | Fee Charged:$ |
| --- | --- | --- |

**Signer's FULL Address**  Phone No.

**Right Thumb Print**
*(When Applicable)*

Notary Service(s) Performed ☐ Jurat ☐ Acknowledgment ☐ Oath

Other(Details)

Date Notarized:  Time:

AM PM

Document:  Document Date:

**IDENTIFICATION**

Type:

☐ Affidavit ☐ Trust ☐ Acknowledgement

☐ Mortgage/Deed ☐ Will ☐ Power of Attorney

☐ Auto Title ☐ Claim ☐ Other: _____

Notary Service Performed at:

Number:

Issued By:

Expires:

Notes/Comments:

Witness Name/Address:  Witness Signature:

Known Personally:

☐ Yes ☐ No

**RECORD NUMBER**
**56**

---

| Name of Signer *(printed)* | Signer's Signature | Fee Charged:$ |
| --- | --- | --- |

**Signer's FULL Address**  Phone No.

**Right Thumb Print**
*(When Applicable)*

Notary Service(s) Performed ☐ Jurat ☐ Acknowledgment ☐ Oath

Other(Details)

Date Notarized:  Time:

AM PM

Document:  Document Date:

**IDENTIFICATION**

Type:

☐ Affidavit ☐ Trust ☐ Acknowledgement

☐ Mortgage/Deed ☐ Will ☐ Power of Attorney

☐ Auto Title ☐ Claim ☐ Other: _____

Notary Service Performed at:

Number:

Issued By:

Expires:

Notes/Comments:

Witness Name/Address:  Witness Signature:

Known Personally:

☐ Yes ☐ No

**RECORD NUMBER**
**57**

| Name of Signer (printed) | Signer's Signature | Fee Charged:$ |
|---|---|---|

**Right Thumb Print** (When Applicable)

Signer's FULL Address

Phone No.

Notary Service(s) Performed ☐Jurat ☐Acknowledgment ☐Oath

Other(Details)

Date Notarized: Time:

AM PM

Notes/Comments:

Document: Document Date:

☐ Affidavit ☐ Trust ☐ Acknowledgement
☐ Mortgage/Deed ☐ Will ☐ Power of Attorney
☐ Auto Title ☐ Claim ☐ Other: _____

Notary Service Performed at:

**IDENTIFICATION**
Type:

Number:

Issued By:

Expires:

**RECORD NUMBER 58**

Witness Name/Address: Witness Signature:

Known Personally:
☐Yes ☐No

---

| Name of Signer (printed) | Signer's Signature | Fee Charged:$ |
|---|---|---|

**Right Thumb Print** (When Applicable)

Signer's FULL Address

Phone No.

Notary Service(s) Performed ☐Jurat ☐Acknowledgment ☐Oath

Other(Details)

Date Notarized: Time:

AM PM

Notes/Comments:

Document: Document Date:

☐ Affidavit ☐ Trust ☐ Acknowledgement
☐ Mortgage/Deed ☐ Will ☐ Power of Attorney
☐ Auto Title ☐ Claim ☐ Other: _____

Notary Service Performed at:

**IDENTIFICATION**
Type:

Number:

Issued By:

Expires:

**RECORD NUMBER 59**

Witness Name/Address: Witness Signature:

Known Personally:
☐Yes ☐No

---

| Name of Signer (printed) | Signer's Signature | Fee Charged:$ |
|---|---|---|

**Right Thumb Print** (When Applicable)

Signer's FULL Address

Phone No.

Notary Service(s) Performed ☐Jurat ☐Acknowledgment ☐Oath

Other(Details)

Date Notarized: Time:

AM PM

Notes/Comments:

Document: Document Date:

☐ Affidavit ☐ Trust ☐ Acknowledgement
☐ Mortgage/Deed ☐ Will ☐ Power of Attorney
☐ Auto Title ☐ Claim ☐ Other: _____

Notary Service Performed at:

**IDENTIFICATION**
Type:

Number:

Issued By:

Expires:

**RECORD NUMBER 60**

Witness Name/Address: Witness Signature:

Known Personally:
☐Yes ☐No

| Name of Signer *(printed)* | Signer's Signature | Fee Charged:$ |
|---|---|---|

**Signer's FULL Address**     Phone No. | Right Thumb Print *(When Applicable)*

| Notary Service(s) Performed | ☐ Jurat | ☐ Acknowledgment | ☐ Oath | Date Notarized:    Time: |
|---|---|---|---|---|

Other(Details)

AM PM

**IDENTIFICATION**

Document:               Document Date:

Type:

☐ Affidavit    ☐ Trust    ☐ Acknowledgement

Number:

☐ Mortgage/Deed    ☐ Will    ☐ Power of Attorney

Issued By:

☐ Auto Title    ☐ Claim    ☐ Other: _____

Notary Service Performed at:

Expires:

Notes/Comments:

| Witness Name/Address: | Witness Signature: | Known Personally: ☐ Yes ☐ No | **RECORD NUMBER 61** |
|---|---|---|---|

---

| Name of Signer *(printed)* | Signer's Signature | Fee Charged:$ |
|---|---|---|

**Signer's FULL Address**     Phone No. | Right Thumb Print *(When Applicable)*

| Notary Service(s) Performed | ☐ Jurat | ☐ Acknowledgment | ☐ Oath | Date Notarized:    Time: |
|---|---|---|---|---|

Other(Details)

AM PM

**IDENTIFICATION**

Document:               Document Date:

Type:

☐ Affidavit    ☐ Trust    ☐ Acknowledgement

Number:

☐ Mortgage/Deed    ☐ Will    ☐ Power of Attorney

Issued By:

☐ Auto Title    ☐ Claim    ☐ Other: _____

Notary Service Performed at:

Expires:

Notes/Comments:

| Witness Name/Address: | Witness Signature: | Known Personally: ☐ Yes ☐ No | **RECORD NUMBER 62** |
|---|---|---|---|

---

| Name of Signer *(printed)* | Signer's Signature | Fee Charged:$ |
|---|---|---|

**Signer's FULL Address**     Phone No. | Right Thumb Print *(When Applicable)*

| Notary Service(s) Performed | ☐ Jurat | ☐ Acknowledgment | ☐ Oath | Date Notarized:    Time: |
|---|---|---|---|---|

Other(Details)

AM PM

**IDENTIFICATION**

Document:               Document Date:

Type:

☐ Affidavit    ☐ Trust    ☐ Acknowledgement

Number:

☐ Mortgage/Deed    ☐ Will    ☐ Power of Attorney

Issued By:

☐ Auto Title    ☐ Claim    ☐ Other: _____

Notary Service Performed at:

Expires:

Notes/Comments:

| Witness Name/Address: | Witness Signature: | Known Personally: ☐ Yes ☐ No | **RECORD NUMBER 63** |
|---|---|---|---|

| Name of Signer *(printed)* | Signer's Signature | Fee Charged:$ |
|---|---|---|

| Right Thumb Print *(When Applicable)* | Signer's FULL Address | Phone No. |
|---|---|---|
| | Notary Service(s) Performed ☐Jurat ☐Acknowledgment ☐Oath<br><br>Other(Details) | Date Notarized: Time:<br><br>AM PM |
| Notes/Comments: | Document: Document Date:<br><br>☐ Affidavit ☐ Trust ☐ Acknowledgement<br>☐ Mortgage/Deed ☐ Will ☐ Power of Attorney<br>☐ Auto Title ☐ Claim ☐ Other: _____<br><br>Notary Service Performed at: | **IDENTIFICATION**<br>Type:<br><br>Number:<br><br>Issued By:<br><br>Expires: |
| **RECORD NUMBER**<br>**64** | Witness Name/Address: Witness Signature: | Known Personally:<br>☐Yes ☐No |

| Name of Signer *(printed)* | Signer's Signature | Fee Charged:$ |
|---|---|---|

| Right Thumb Print *(When Applicable)* | Signer's FULL Address | Phone No. |
|---|---|---|
| | Notary Service(s) Performed ☐Jurat ☐Acknowledgment ☐Oath<br><br>Other(Details) | Date Notarized: Time:<br><br>AM PM |
| Notes/Comments: | Document: Document Date:<br><br>☐ Affidavit ☐ Trust ☐ Acknowledgement<br>☐ Mortgage/Deed ☐ Will ☐ Power of Attorney<br>☐ Auto Title ☐ Claim ☐ Other: _____<br><br>Notary Service Performed at: | **IDENTIFICATION**<br>Type:<br><br>Number:<br><br>Issued By:<br><br>Expires: |
| **RECORD NUMBER**<br>**65** | Witness Name/Address: Witness Signature: | Known Personally:<br>☐Yes ☐No |

| Name of Signer *(printed)* | Signer's Signature | Fee Charged:$ |
|---|---|---|

| Right Thumb Print *(When Applicable)* | Signer's FULL Address | Phone No. |
|---|---|---|
| | Notary Service(s) Performed ☐Jurat ☐Acknowledgment ☐Oath<br><br>Other(Details) | Date Notarized: Time:<br><br>AM PM |
| Notes/Comments: | Document: Document Date:<br><br>☐ Affidavit ☐ Trust ☐ Acknowledgement<br>☐ Mortgage/Deed ☐ Will ☐ Power of Attorney<br>☐ Auto Title ☐ Claim ☐ Other: _____<br><br>Notary Service Performed at: | **IDENTIFICATION**<br>Type:<br><br>Number:<br><br>Issued By:<br><br>Expires: |
| **RECORD NUMBER**<br>**66** | Witness Name/Address: Witness Signature: | Known Personally:<br>☐Yes ☐No |

| Name of Signer *(printed)* | Signer's Signature | Fee Charged:$ |
|---|---|---|

**Signer's FULL Address**  Phone No.  Right Thumb Print *(When Applicable)*

Notary Service(s) Performed ☐ Jurat ☐ Acknowledgment ☐ Oath  | Date Notarized:  Time:  AM PM

Other(Details)

**IDENTIFICATION**

Document:  Document Date:  Type:

☐ Affidavit ☐ Trust ☐ Acknowledgement  Number:  Notes/Comments:
☐ Mortgage/Deed ☐ Will ☐ Power of Attorney  Issued By:
☐ Auto Title ☐ Claim ☐ Other: _____  

Notary Service Performed at:  Expires:

Witness Name/Address:  Witness Signature:  Known Personally:  ☐ Yes ☐ No

**RECORD NUMBER 67**

---

| Name of Signer *(printed)* | Signer's Signature | Fee Charged:$ |
|---|---|---|

**Signer's FULL Address**  Phone No.  Right Thumb Print *(When Applicable)*

Notary Service(s) Performed ☐ Jurat ☐ Acknowledgment ☐ Oath  | Date Notarized:  Time:  AM PM

Other(Details)

**IDENTIFICATION**

Document:  Document Date:  Type:

☐ Affidavit ☐ Trust ☐ Acknowledgement  Number:  Notes/Comments:
☐ Mortgage/Deed ☐ Will ☐ Power of Attorney  Issued By:
☐ Auto Title ☐ Claim ☐ Other: _____  

Notary Service Performed at:  Expires:

Witness Name/Address:  Witness Signature:  Known Personally:  ☐ Yes ☐ No

**RECORD NUMBER 68**

---

| Name of Signer *(printed)* | Signer's Signature | Fee Charged:$ |
|---|---|---|

**Signer's FULL Address**  Phone No.  Right Thumb Print *(When Applicable)*

Notary Service(s) Performed ☐ Jurat ☐ Acknowledgment ☐ Oath  | Date Notarized:  Time:  AM PM

Other(Details)

**IDENTIFICATION**

Document:  Document Date:  Type:

☐ Affidavit ☐ Trust ☐ Acknowledgement  Number:  Notes/Comments:
☐ Mortgage/Deed ☐ Will ☐ Power of Attorney  Issued By:
☐ Auto Title ☐ Claim ☐ Other: _____  

Notary Service Performed at:  Expires:

Witness Name/Address:  Witness Signature:  Known Personally:  ☐ Yes ☐ No

**RECORD NUMBER 69**

| Name of Signer (printed) | Signer's Signature | Fee Charged: $ |
|---|---|---|

| Right Thumb Print (When Applicable) | Signer's FULL Address | | Phone No. |
|---|---|---|---|
| | Notary Service(s) Performed ☐Jurat ☐Acknowledgment ☐Oath<br>Other(Details) | | Date Notarized: Time:<br><br>AM PM |
| Notes/Comments: | Document: Document Date:<br><br>☐ Affidavit ☐ Trust ☐ Acknowledgement<br>☐ Mortgage/Deed ☐ Will ☐ Power of Attorney<br>☐ Auto Title ☐ Claim ☐ Other: _____<br>Notary Service Performed at: | | IDENTIFICATION<br>Type:<br>Number:<br>Issued By:<br>Expires: |
| **RECORD NUMBER 70** | Witness Name/Address: | Witness Signature: | Known Personally:<br>☐Yes ☐No |

| Name of Signer (printed) | Signer's Signature | Fee Charged: $ |
|---|---|---|

| Right Thumb Print (When Applicable) | Signer's FULL Address | | Phone No. |
|---|---|---|---|
| | Notary Service(s) Performed ☐Jurat ☐Acknowledgment ☐Oath<br>Other(Details) | | Date Notarized: Time:<br><br>AM PM |
| Notes/Comments: | Document: Document Date:<br><br>☐ Affidavit ☐ Trust ☐ Acknowledgement<br>☐ Mortgage/Deed ☐ Will ☐ Power of Attorney<br>☐ Auto Title ☐ Claim ☐ Other: _____<br>Notary Service Performed at: | | IDENTIFICATION<br>Type:<br>Number:<br>Issued By:<br>Expires: |
| **RECORD NUMBER 71** | Witness Name/Address: | Witness Signature: | Known Personally:<br>☐Yes ☐No |

| Name of Signer (printed) | Signer's Signature | Fee Charged: $ |
|---|---|---|

| Right Thumb Print (When Applicable) | Signer's FULL Address | | Phone No. |
|---|---|---|---|
| | Notary Service(s) Performed ☐Jurat ☐Acknowledgment ☐Oath<br>Other(Details) | | Date Notarized: Time:<br><br>AM PM |
| Notes/Comments: | Document: Document Date:<br><br>☐ Affidavit ☐ Trust ☐ Acknowledgement<br>☐ Mortgage/Deed ☐ Will ☐ Power of Attorney<br>☐ Auto Title ☐ Claim ☐ Other: _____<br>Notary Service Performed at: | | IDENTIFICATION<br>Type:<br>Number:<br>Issued By:<br>Expires: |
| **RECORD NUMBER 72** | Witness Name/Address: | Witness Signature: | Known Personally:<br>☐Yes ☐No |

## Record Number 73

Name of Signer *(printed)*

Signer's Signature

Fee Charged: $

Signer's FULL Address

Phone No.

Right Thumb Print *(When Applicable)*

Notary Service(s) Performed ☐ Jurat ☐ Acknowledgment ☐ Oath

Other(Details)

Date Notarized: Time:

AM PM

**IDENTIFICATION**

Document:

Document Date:

☐ Affidavit ☐ Trust ☐ Acknowledgement
☐ Mortgage/Deed ☐ Will ☐ Power of Attorney
☐ Auto Title ☐ Claim ☐ Other: _____

Notary Service Performed at:

Type:

Number:

Issued By:

Expires:

Notes/Comments:

Witness Name/Address:

Witness Signature:

Known Personally:

☐ Yes ☐ No

**RECORD NUMBER 73**

---

## Record Number 74

Name of Signer *(printed)*

Signer's Signature

Fee Charged: $

Signer's FULL Address

Phone No.

Right Thumb Print *(When Applicable)*

Notary Service(s) Performed ☐ Jurat ☐ Acknowledgment ☐ Oath

Other(Details)

Date Notarized: Time:

AM PM

**IDENTIFICATION**

Document:

Document Date:

☐ Affidavit ☐ Trust ☐ Acknowledgement
☐ Mortgage/Deed ☐ Will ☐ Power of Attorney
☐ Auto Title ☐ Claim ☐ Other: _____

Notary Service Performed at:

Type:

Number:

Issued By:

Expires:

Notes/Comments:

Witness Name/Address:

Witness Signature:

Known Personally:

☐ Yes ☐ No

**RECORD NUMBER 74**

---

## Record Number 75

Name of Signer *(printed)*

Signer's Signature

Fee Charged: $

Signer's FULL Address

Phone No.

Right Thumb Print *(When Applicable)*

Notary Service(s) Performed ☐ Jurat ☐ Acknowledgment ☐ Oath

Other(Details)

Date Notarized: Time:

AM PM

**IDENTIFICATION**

Document:

Document Date:

☐ Affidavit ☐ Trust ☐ Acknowledgement
☐ Mortgage/Deed ☐ Will ☐ Power of Attorney
☐ Auto Title ☐ Claim ☐ Other: _____

Notary Service Performed at:

Type:

Number:

Issued By:

Expires:

Notes/Comments:

Witness Name/Address:

Witness Signature:

Known Personally:

☐ Yes ☐ No

**RECORD NUMBER 75**

| Name of Signer (printed) | Signer's Signature | Fee Charged:$ |
| --- | --- | --- |

**Right Thumb Print** (When Applicable)

Signer's FULL Address

Phone No.

| Notary Service(s) Performed | ☐Jurat | ☐Acknowledgment | ☐Oath | Date Notarized: | Time: |
| --- | --- | --- | --- | --- | --- |

Other(Details)

AM PM

**IDENTIFICATION**

Notes/Comments:

Document:                             Document Date:

Type:

☐ Affidavit      ☐ Trust      ☐ Acknowledgement

Number:

☐ Mortgage/Deed    ☐ Will      ☐ Power of Attorney

Issued By:

☐ Auto Title      ☐ Claim      ☐ Other: _____

Notary Service Performed at:

Expires:

| **RECORD NUMBER 76** | Witness Name/Address: | Witness Signature: | Known Personally: ☐Yes ☐No |
| --- | --- | --- | --- |

---

| Name of Signer (printed) | Signer's Signature | Fee Charged:$ |
| --- | --- | --- |

**Right Thumb Print** (When Applicable)

Signer's FULL Address

Phone No.

| Notary Service(s) Performed | ☐Jurat | ☐Acknowledgment | ☐Oath | Date Notarized: | Time: |
| --- | --- | --- | --- | --- | --- |

Other(Details)

AM PM

**IDENTIFICATION**

Notes/Comments:

Document:                             Document Date:

Type:

☐ Affidavit      ☐ Trust      ☐ Acknowledgement

Number:

☐ Mortgage/Deed    ☐ Will      ☐ Power of Attorney

Issued By:

☐ Auto Title      ☐ Claim      ☐ Other: _____

Notary Service Performed at:

Expires:

| **RECORD NUMBER 77** | Witness Name/Address: | Witness Signature: | Known Personally: ☐Yes ☐No |
| --- | --- | --- | --- |

---

| Name of Signer (printed) | Signer's Signature | Fee Charged:$ |
| --- | --- | --- |

**Right Thumb Print** (When Applicable)

Signer's FULL Address

Phone No.

| Notary Service(s) Performed | ☐Jurat | ☐Acknowledgment | ☐Oath | Date Notarized: | Time: |
| --- | --- | --- | --- | --- | --- |

Other(Details)

AM PM

**IDENTIFICATION**

Notes/Comments:

Document:                             Document Date:

Type:

☐ Affidavit      ☐ Trust      ☐ Acknowledgement

Number:

☐ Mortgage/Deed    ☐ Will      ☐ Power of Attorney

Issued By:

☐ Auto Title      ☐ Claim      ☐ Other: _____

Notary Service Performed at:

Expires:

| **RECORD NUMBER 78** | Witness Name/Address: | Witness Signature: | Known Personally: ☐Yes ☐No |
| --- | --- | --- | --- |

## Record Number 79

**Name of Signer** *(printed)* | **Signer's Signature** | **Fee Charged:** $

**Signer's FULL Address** | **Phone No.** | **Right Thumb Print** *(When Applicable)*

**Notary Service(s) Performed** ☐ Jurat ☐ Acknowledgment ☐ Oath | **Date Notarized:** **Time:** AM PM

Other(Details)

**Document:** **Document Date:**

☐ Affidavit ☐ Trust ☐ Acknowledgement
☐ Mortgage/Deed ☐ Will ☐ Power of Attorney
☐ Auto Title ☐ Claim ☐ Other: _____

**Notary Service Performed at:**

**IDENTIFICATION**
Type:
Number:
Issued By:
Expires:

Notes/Comments:

**Witness Name/Address:** | **Witness Signature:** | **Known Personally:** ☐ Yes ☐ No | **RECORD NUMBER 79**

---

## Record Number 80

**Name of Signer** *(printed)* | **Signer's Signature** | **Fee Charged:** $

**Signer's FULL Address** | **Phone No.** | **Right Thumb Print** *(When Applicable)*

**Notary Service(s) Performed** ☐ Jurat ☐ Acknowledgment ☐ Oath | **Date Notarized:** **Time:** AM PM

Other(Details)

**Document:** **Document Date:**

☐ Affidavit ☐ Trust ☐ Acknowledgement
☐ Mortgage/Deed ☐ Will ☐ Power of Attorney
☐ Auto Title ☐ Claim ☐ Other: _____

**Notary Service Performed at:**

**IDENTIFICATION**
Type:
Number:
Issued By:
Expires:

Notes/Comments:

**Witness Name/Address:** | **Witness Signature:** | **Known Personally:** ☐ Yes ☐ No | **RECORD NUMBER 80**

---

## Record Number 81

**Name of Signer** *(printed)* | **Signer's Signature** | **Fee Charged:** $

**Signer's FULL Address** | **Phone No.** | **Right Thumb Print** *(When Applicable)*

**Notary Service(s) Performed** ☐ Jurat ☐ Acknowledgment ☐ Oath | **Date Notarized:** **Time:** AM PM

Other(Details)

**Document:** **Document Date:**

☐ Affidavit ☐ Trust ☐ Acknowledgement
☐ Mortgage/Deed ☐ Will ☐ Power of Attorney
☐ Auto Title ☐ Claim ☐ Other: _____

**Notary Service Performed at:**

**IDENTIFICATION**
Type:
Number:
Issued By:
Expires:

Notes/Comments:

**Witness Name/Address:** | **Witness Signature:** | **Known Personally:** ☐ Yes ☐ No | **RECORD NUMBER 81**

| Name of Signer *(printed)* | Signer's Signature | Fee Charged:$ |
|---|---|---|

| Right Thumb Print *(When Applicable)* | Signer's FULL Address | Phone No. |
|---|---|---|

Notary Service(s) Performed ☐Jurat ☐Acknowledgment ☐Oath

Other(Details)

Date Notarized:     Time:

AM PM

**IDENTIFICATION**

Notes/Comments:

Document:                  Document Date:

Type:

☐ Affidavit     ☐ Trust     ☐ Acknowledgement

☐ Mortgage/Deed     ☐ Will     ☐ Power of Attorney

☐ Auto Title     ☐ Claim     ☐ Other: _____

Number:

Issued By:

Notary Service Performed at:

Expires:

**RECORD NUMBER 82**

Witness Name/Address:        Witness Signature:

Known Personally:

☐Yes ☐No

---

| Name of Signer *(printed)* | Signer's Signature | Fee Charged:$ |
|---|---|---|

| Right Thumb Print *(When Applicable)* | Signer's FULL Address | Phone No. |
|---|---|---|

Notary Service(s) Performed ☐Jurat ☐Acknowledgment ☐Oath

Other(Details)

Date Notarized:     Time:

AM PM

**IDENTIFICATION**

Notes/Comments:

Document:                  Document Date:

Type:

☐ Affidavit     ☐ Trust     ☐ Acknowledgement

☐ Mortgage/Deed     ☐ Will     ☐ Power of Attorney

☐ Auto Title     ☐ Claim     ☐ Other: _____

Number:

Issued By:

Notary Service Performed at:

Expires:

**RECORD NUMBER 83**

Witness Name/Address:        Witness Signature:

Known Personally:

☐Yes ☐No

---

| Name of Signer *(printed)* | Signer's Signature | Fee Charged:$ |
|---|---|---|

| Right Thumb Print *(When Applicable)* | Signer's FULL Address | Phone No. |
|---|---|---|

Notary Service(s) Performed ☐Jurat ☐Acknowledgment ☐Oath

Other(Details)

Date Notarized:     Time:

AM PM

**IDENTIFICATION**

Notes/Comments:

Document:                  Document Date:

Type:

☐ Affidavit     ☐ Trust     ☐ Acknowledgement

☐ Mortgage/Deed     ☐ Will     ☐ Power of Attorney

☐ Auto Title     ☐ Claim     ☐ Other: _____

Number:

Issued By:

Notary Service Performed at:

Expires:

**RECORD NUMBER 84**

Witness Name/Address:        Witness Signature:

Known Personally:

☐Yes ☐No

## Record Number 85

**Name of Signer** *(printed)*

**Signer's Signature**

**Fee Charged:** $

**Signer's FULL Address**

**Phone No.**

**Right Thumb Print** *(When Applicable)*

**Notary Service(s) Performed**  ☐ Jurat  ☐ Acknowledgment  ☐ Oath

**Other(Details)**

**Date Notarized:**     **Time:**

AM  PM

**Document:**     **Document Date:**

**IDENTIFICATION**

Type:

☐ Affidavit  ☐ Trust  ☐ Acknowledgement

☐ Mortgage/Deed  ☐ Will  ☐ Power of Attorney

☐ Auto Title  ☐ Claim  ☐ Other: _____

Number:

Issued By:

**Notary Service Performed at:**

Expires:

**Notes/Comments:**

**Witness Name/Address:**     **Witness Signature:**

**Known Personally:**

☐ **Yes**  ☐ **No**

**RECORD NUMBER 85**

---

## Record Number 86

**Name of Signer** *(printed)*

**Signer's Signature**

**Fee Charged:** $

**Signer's FULL Address**

**Phone No.**

**Right Thumb Print** *(When Applicable)*

**Notary Service(s) Performed**  ☐ Jurat  ☐ Acknowledgment  ☐ Oath

**Other(Details)**

**Date Notarized:**     **Time:**

AM  PM

**Document:**     **Document Date:**

**IDENTIFICATION**

Type:

☐ Affidavit  ☐ Trust  ☐ Acknowledgement

☐ Mortgage/Deed  ☐ Will  ☐ Power of Attorney

☐ Auto Title  ☐ Claim  ☐ Other: _____

Number:

Issued By:

**Notary Service Performed at:**

Expires:

**Notes/Comments:**

**Witness Name/Address:**     **Witness Signature:**

**Known Personally:**

☐ **Yes**  ☐ **No**

**RECORD NUMBER 86**

---

## Record Number 87

**Name of Signer** *(printed)*

**Signer's Signature**

**Fee Charged:** $

**Signer's FULL Address**

**Phone No.**

**Right Thumb Print** *(When Applicable)*

**Notary Service(s) Performed**  ☐ Jurat  ☐ Acknowledgment  ☐ Oath

**Other(Details)**

**Date Notarized:**     **Time:**

AM  PM

**Document:**     **Document Date:**

**IDENTIFICATION**

Type:

☐ Affidavit  ☐ Trust  ☐ Acknowledgement

☐ Mortgage/Deed  ☐ Will  ☐ Power of Attorney

☐ Auto Title  ☐ Claim  ☐ Other: _____

Number:

Issued By:

**Notary Service Performed at:**

Expires:

**Notes/Comments:**

**Witness Name/Address:**     **Witness Signature:**

**Known Personally:**

☐ **Yes**  ☐ **No**

**RECORD NUMBER 87**

| Name of Signer (printed) | Signer's Signature | Fee Charged: $ |
|---|---|---|

**Right Thumb Print** (When Applicable)

Signer's FULL Address        Phone No.

Notary Service(s) Performed   ☐ Jurat   ☐ Acknowledgment   ☐ Oath

Other(Details)

Date Notarized:    Time:

AM PM

**IDENTIFICATION**

Type:

Number:

Issued By:

Expires:

Notes/Comments:

Document:                   Document Date:

☐ Affidavit    ☐ Trust    ☐ Acknowledgement

☐ Mortgage/Deed    ☐ Will    ☐ Power of Attorney

☐ Auto Title    ☐ Claim    ☐ Other: _____

Notary Service Performed at:

**RECORD NUMBER 88**

Witness Name/Address:            Witness Signature:

Known Personally:

☐ Yes   ☐ No

---

| Name of Signer (printed) | Signer's Signature | Fee Charged: $ |
|---|---|---|

**Right Thumb Print** (When Applicable)

Signer's FULL Address        Phone No.

Notary Service(s) Performed   ☐ Jurat   ☐ Acknowledgment   ☐ Oath

Other(Details)

Date Notarized:    Time:

AM PM

**IDENTIFICATION**

Type:

Number:

Issued By:

Expires:

Notes/Comments:

Document:                   Document Date:

☐ Affidavit    ☐ Trust    ☐ Acknowledgement

☐ Mortgage/Deed    ☐ Will    ☐ Power of Attorney

☐ Auto Title    ☐ Claim    ☐ Other: _____

Notary Service Performed at:

**RECORD NUMBER 89**

Witness Name/Address:            Witness Signature:

Known Personally:

☐ Yes   ☐ No

---

| Name of Signer (printed) | Signer's Signature | Fee Charged: $ |
|---|---|---|

**Right Thumb Print** (When Applicable)

Signer's FULL Address        Phone No.

Notary Service(s) Performed   ☐ Jurat   ☐ Acknowledgment   ☐ Oath

Other(Details)

Date Notarized:    Time:

AM PM

**IDENTIFICATION**

Type:

Number:

Issued By:

Expires:

Notes/Comments:

Document:                   Document Date:

☐ Affidavit    ☐ Trust    ☐ Acknowledgement

☐ Mortgage/Deed    ☐ Will    ☐ Power of Attorney

☐ Auto Title    ☐ Claim    ☐ Other: _____

Notary Service Performed at:

**RECORD NUMBER 90**

Witness Name/Address:            Witness Signature:

Known Personally:

☐ Yes   ☐ No

| Name of Signer *(printed)* | Signer's Signature | Fee Charged:$ |
|---|---|---|

Signer's FULL Address  Phone No.

Right Thumb Print
*(When Applicable)*

Notary Service(s) Performed  ☐ Jurat  ☐ Acknowledgment  ☐ Oath

Other(Details)

Date Notarized:  Time:

AM PM

Document:  Document Date:

**IDENTIFICATION**
Type:

☐ Affidavit  ☐ Trust  ☐ Acknowledgement
☐ Mortgage/Deed  ☐ Will  ☐ Power of Attorney
☐ Auto Title  ☐ Claim  ☐ Other: _____

Notary Service Performed at:

Number:

Issued By:

Expires:

Notes/Comments:

Witness Name/Address:  Witness Signature:

Known Personally:
☐ Yes  ☐ No

**RECORD NUMBER
91**

---

| Name of Signer *(printed)* | Signer's Signature | Fee Charged:$ |
|---|---|---|

Signer's FULL Address  Phone No.

Right Thumb Print
*(When Applicable)*

Notary Service(s) Performed  ☐ Jurat  ☐ Acknowledgment  ☐ Oath

Other(Details)

Date Notarized:  Time:

AM PM

Document:  Document Date:

**IDENTIFICATION**
Type:

☐ Affidavit  ☐ Trust  ☐ Acknowledgement
☐ Mortgage/Deed  ☐ Will  ☐ Power of Attorney
☐ Auto Title  ☐ Claim  ☐ Other: _____

Notary Service Performed at:

Number:

Issued By:

Expires:

Notes/Comments:

Witness Name/Address:  Witness Signature:

Known Personally:
☐ Yes  ☐ No

**RECORD NUMBER
92**

---

| Name of Signer *(printed)* | Signer's Signature | Fee Charged:$ |
|---|---|---|

Signer's FULL Address  Phone No.

Right Thumb Print
*(When Applicable)*

Notary Service(s) Performed  ☐ Jurat  ☐ Acknowledgment  ☐ Oath

Other(Details)

Date Notarized:  Time:

AM PM

Document:  Document Date:

**IDENTIFICATION**
Type:

☐ Affidavit  ☐ Trust  ☐ Acknowledgement
☐ Mortgage/Deed  ☐ Will  ☐ Power of Attorney
☐ Auto Title  ☐ Claim  ☐ Other: _____

Notary Service Performed at:

Number:

Issued By:

Expires:

Notes/Comments:

Witness Name/Address:  Witness Signature:

Known Personally:
☐ Yes  ☐ No

**RECORD NUMBER
93**

| Name of Signer *(printed)* | Signer's Signature | Fee Charged:$ |
|---|---|---|

| Right Thumb Print *(When Applicable)* | Signer's FULL Address | Phone No. |
|---|---|---|

| | Notary Service(s) Performed ☐Jurat ☐Acknowledgment ☐Oath<br><br>Other(Details) | Date Notarized: Time:<br><br>AM PM |
|---|---|---|

| Notes/Comments: | Document: Document Date:<br>☐ Affidavit ☐ Trust ☐ Acknowledgement<br>☐ Mortgage/Deed ☐ Will ☐ Power of Attorney<br>☐ Auto Title ☐ Claim ☐ Other: _____<br>Notary Service Performed at: | **IDENTIFICATION**<br>Type:<br>Number:<br>Issued By:<br>Expires: |
|---|---|---|

| **RECORD NUMBER 94** | Witness Name/Address: Witness Signature: | Known Personally:<br>☐Yes ☐No |
|---|---|---|

---

| Name of Signer *(printed)* | Signer's Signature | Fee Charged:$ |
|---|---|---|

| Right Thumb Print *(When Applicable)* | Signer's FULL Address | Phone No. |
|---|---|---|

| | Notary Service(s) Performed ☐Jurat ☐Acknowledgment ☐Oath<br><br>Other(Details) | Date Notarized: Time:<br><br>AM PM |
|---|---|---|

| Notes/Comments: | Document: Document Date:<br>☐ Affidavit ☐ Trust ☐ Acknowledgement<br>☐ Mortgage/Deed ☐ Will ☐ Power of Attorney<br>☐ Auto Title ☐ Claim ☐ Other: _____<br>Notary Service Performed at: | **IDENTIFICATION**<br>Type:<br>Number:<br>Issued By:<br>Expires: |
|---|---|---|

| **RECORD NUMBER 95** | Witness Name/Address: Witness Signature: | Known Personally:<br>☐Yes ☐No |
|---|---|---|

---

| Name of Signer *(printed)* | Signer's Signature | Fee Charged:$ |
|---|---|---|

| Right Thumb Print *(When Applicable)* | Signer's FULL Address | Phone No. |
|---|---|---|

| | Notary Service(s) Performed ☐Jurat ☐Acknowledgment ☐Oath<br><br>Other(Details) | Date Notarized: Time:<br><br>AM PM |
|---|---|---|

| Notes/Comments: | Document: Document Date:<br>☐ Affidavit ☐ Trust ☐ Acknowledgement<br>☐ Mortgage/Deed ☐ Will ☐ Power of Attorney<br>☐ Auto Title ☐ Claim ☐ Other: _____<br>Notary Service Performed at: | **IDENTIFICATION**<br>Type:<br>Number:<br>Issued By:<br>Expires: |
|---|---|---|

| **RECORD NUMBER 96** | Witness Name/Address: Witness Signature: | Known Personally:<br>☐Yes ☐No |
|---|---|---|

| Name of Signer *(printed)* | Signer's Signature | Fee Charged: $ |
|---|---|---|

**Signer's FULL Address**      Phone No.     Right Thumb Print *(When Applicable)*

Notary Service(s) Performed   ☐ Jurat   ☐ Acknowledgment   ☐ Oath    Date Notarized:    Time:

Other(Details)

       AM PM

Document:      Document Date:     **IDENTIFICATION**

Type:

☐ Affidavit    ☐ Trust    ☐ Acknowledgement    Notes/Comments:
☐ Mortgage/Deed    ☐ Will    ☐ Power of Attorney    Number:
☐ Auto Title    ☐ Claim    ☐ Other: _____

Issued By:

Notary Service Performed at:     Expires:

Witness Name/Address:     Witness Signature:     Known Personally:    **RECORD NUMBER**
     ☐ Yes   ☐ No    **97**

---

| Name of Signer *(printed)* | Signer's Signature | Fee Charged: $ |
|---|---|---|

**Signer's FULL Address**      Phone No.     Right Thumb Print *(When Applicable)*

Notary Service(s) Performed   ☐ Jurat   ☐ Acknowledgment   ☐ Oath    Date Notarized:    Time:

Other(Details)

       AM PM

Document:      Document Date:     **IDENTIFICATION**

Type:

☐ Affidavit    ☐ Trust    ☐ Acknowledgement    Notes/Comments:
☐ Mortgage/Deed    ☐ Will    ☐ Power of Attorney    Number:
☐ Auto Title    ☐ Claim    ☐ Other: _____

Issued By:

Notary Service Performed at:     Expires:

Witness Name/Address:     Witness Signature:     Known Personally:    **RECORD NUMBER**
     ☐ Yes   ☐ No    **98**

---

| Name of Signer *(printed)* | Signer's Signature | Fee Charged: $ |
|---|---|---|

**Signer's FULL Address**      Phone No.     Right Thumb Print *(When Applicable)*

Notary Service(s) Performed   ☐ Jurat   ☐ Acknowledgment   ☐ Oath    Date Notarized:    Time:

Other(Details)

       AM PM

Document:      Document Date:     **IDENTIFICATION**

Type:

☐ Affidavit    ☐ Trust    ☐ Acknowledgement    Notes/Comments:
☐ Mortgage/Deed    ☐ Will    ☐ Power of Attorney    Number:
☐ Auto Title    ☐ Claim    ☐ Other: _____

Issued By:

Notary Service Performed at:     Expires:

Witness Name/Address:     Witness Signature:     Known Personally:    **RECORD NUMBER**
     ☐ Yes   ☐ No    **99**

| Name of Signer (printed) | Signer's Signature | Fee Charged:$ |
|---|---|---|

| Right Thumb Print (When Applicable) | Signer's FULL Address | Phone No. |
|---|---|---|
| | Notary Service(s) Performed ☐Jurat ☐Acknowledgment ☐Oath<br>Other(Details) | Date Notarized: Time:<br>AM PM |
| Notes/Comments: | Document: Document Date:<br>☐ Affidavit ☐ Trust ☐ Acknowledgement<br>☐ Mortgage/Deed ☐ Will ☐ Power of Attorney<br>☐ Auto Title ☐ Claim ☐ Other: _____<br>Notary Service Performed at: | **IDENTIFICATION**<br>Type:<br>Number:<br>Issued By:<br>Expires: |
| **RECORD NUMBER 100** | Witness Name/Address: Witness Signature: | Known Personally:<br>☐Yes ☐No |

| Name of Signer (printed) | Signer's Signature | Fee Charged:$ |
|---|---|---|

| Right Thumb Print (When Applicable) | Signer's FULL Address | Phone No. |
|---|---|---|
| | Notary Service(s) Performed ☐Jurat ☐Acknowledgment ☐Oath<br>Other(Details) | Date Notarized: Time:<br>AM PM |
| Notes/Comments: | Document: Document Date:<br>☐ Affidavit ☐ Trust ☐ Acknowledgement<br>☐ Mortgage/Deed ☐ Will ☐ Power of Attorney<br>☐ Auto Title ☐ Claim ☐ Other: _____<br>Notary Service Performed at: | **IDENTIFICATION**<br>Type:<br>Number:<br>Issued By:<br>Expires: |
| **RECORD NUMBER 101** | Witness Name/Address: Witness Signature: | Known Personally:<br>☐Yes ☐No |

| Name of Signer (printed) | Signer's Signature | Fee Charged:$ |
|---|---|---|

| Right Thumb Print (When Applicable) | Signer's FULL Address | Phone No. |
|---|---|---|
| | Notary Service(s) Performed ☐Jurat ☐Acknowledgment ☐Oath<br>Other(Details) | Date Notarized: Time:<br>AM PM |
| Notes/Comments: | Document: Document Date:<br>☐ Affidavit ☐ Trust ☐ Acknowledgement<br>☐ Mortgage/Deed ☐ Will ☐ Power of Attorney<br>☐ Auto Title ☐ Claim ☐ Other: _____<br>Notary Service Performed at: | **IDENTIFICATION**<br>Type:<br>Number:<br>Issued By:<br>Expires: |
| **RECORD NUMBER 102** | Witness Name/Address: Witness Signature: | Known Personally:<br>☐Yes ☐No |

| Name of Signer *(printed)* | Signer's Signature | Fee Charged:$ |
|---|---|---|

**Signer's FULL Address**  Phone No.  | Right Thumb Print *(When Applicable)*

| Notary Service(s) Performed ☐ Jurat ☐ Acknowledgment ☐ Oath | Date Notarized:  Time: |
|---|---|

Other(Details)

AM PM

**Document:**  Document Date:

**IDENTIFICATION**
Type:

☐ Affidavit ☐ Trust ☐ Acknowledgement

Number:

☐ Mortgage/Deed ☐ Will ☐ Power of Attorney

☐ Auto Title ☐ Claim ☐ Other: _____

Issued By:

Notary Service Performed at:

Expires:

Notes/Comments:

Witness Name/Address:  Witness Signature:  Known Personally:  ☐ Yes ☐ No

**RECORD NUMBER 103**

---

| Name of Signer *(printed)* | Signer's Signature | Fee Charged:$ |
|---|---|---|

**Signer's FULL Address**  Phone No.  | Right Thumb Print *(When Applicable)*

| Notary Service(s) Performed ☐ Jurat ☐ Acknowledgment ☐ Oath | Date Notarized:  Time: |
|---|---|

Other(Details)

AM PM

**Document:**  Document Date:

**IDENTIFICATION**
Type:

☐ Affidavit ☐ Trust ☐ Acknowledgement

Number:

☐ Mortgage/Deed ☐ Will ☐ Power of Attorney

☐ Auto Title ☐ Claim ☐ Other: _____

Issued By:

Notary Service Performed at:

Expires:

Notes/Comments:

Witness Name/Address:  Witness Signature:  Known Personally:  ☐ Yes ☐ No

**RECORD NUMBER 104**

---

| Name of Signer *(printed)* | Signer's Signature | Fee Charged:$ |
|---|---|---|

**Signer's FULL Address**  Phone No.  | Right Thumb Print *(When Applicable)*

| Notary Service(s) Performed ☐ Jurat ☐ Acknowledgment ☐ Oath | Date Notarized:  Time: |
|---|---|

Other(Details)

AM PM

**Document:**  Document Date:

**IDENTIFICATION**
Type:

☐ Affidavit ☐ Trust ☐ Acknowledgement

Number:

☐ Mortgage/Deed ☐ Will ☐ Power of Attorney

☐ Auto Title ☐ Claim ☐ Other: _____

Issued By:

Notary Service Performed at:

Expires:

Notes/Comments:

Witness Name/Address:  Witness Signature:  Known Personally:  ☐ Yes ☐ No

**RECORD NUMBER 105**

| Name of Signer (printed) | Signer's Signature | Fee Charged:$ |
|---|---|---|

| Right Thumb Print (When Applicable) | Signer's FULL Address | Phone No. |
|---|---|---|

**Notary Service(s) Performed** ☐ Jurat ☐ Acknowledgment ☐ Oath

Other(Details)

| | Date Notarized: | Time: |
|---|---|---|
| | | AM PM |

**Document:** Document Date:

☐ Affidavit ☐ Trust ☐ Acknowledgement
☐ Mortgage/Deed ☐ Will ☐ Power of Attorney
☐ Auto Title ☐ Claim ☐ Other: _____

Notary Service Performed at:

**IDENTIFICATION**
Type:

Number:

Issued By:

Expires:

Notes/Comments:

**RECORD NUMBER 106**

Witness Name/Address: Witness Signature:

Known Personally: ☐Yes ☐No

---

| Name of Signer (printed) | Signer's Signature | Fee Charged:$ |
|---|---|---|

| Right Thumb Print (When Applicable) | Signer's FULL Address | Phone No. |
|---|---|---|

**Notary Service(s) Performed** ☐ Jurat ☐ Acknowledgment ☐ Oath

Other(Details)

| | Date Notarized: | Time: |
|---|---|---|
| | | AM PM |

**Document:** Document Date:

☐ Affidavit ☐ Trust ☐ Acknowledgement
☐ Mortgage/Deed ☐ Will ☐ Power of Attorney
☐ Auto Title ☐ Claim ☐ Other: _____

Notary Service Performed at:

**IDENTIFICATION**
Type:

Number:

Issued By:

Expires:

Notes/Comments:

**RECORD NUMBER 107**

Witness Name/Address: Witness Signature:

Known Personally: ☐Yes ☐No

---

| Name of Signer (printed) | Signer's Signature | Fee Charged:$ |
|---|---|---|

| Right Thumb Print (When Applicable) | Signer's FULL Address | Phone No. |
|---|---|---|

**Notary Service(s) Performed** ☐ Jurat ☐ Acknowledgment ☐ Oath

Other(Details)

| | Date Notarized: | Time: |
|---|---|---|
| | | AM PM |

**Document:** Document Date:

☐ Affidavit ☐ Trust ☐ Acknowledgement
☐ Mortgage/Deed ☐ Will ☐ Power of Attorney
☐ Auto Title ☐ Claim ☐ Other: _____

Notary Service Performed at:

**IDENTIFICATION**
Type:

Number:

Issued By:

Expires:

Notes/Comments:

**RECORD NUMBER 108**

Witness Name/Address: Witness Signature:

Known Personally: ☐Yes ☐No

## RECORD NUMBER 109

| Name of Signer (printed) | Signer's Signature | Fee Charged:$ |
|---|---|---|

Signer's FULL Address      Phone No.      Right Thumb Print *(When Applicable)*

Notary Service(s) Performed   ☐ Jurat   ☐ Acknowledgment   ☐ Oath

Other(Details)

Date Notarized:     Time:     AM PM

Document:     Document Date:

☐ Affidavit    ☐ Trust    ☐ Acknowledgement
☐ Mortgage/Deed    ☐ Will    ☐ Power of Attorney
☐ Auto Title    ☐ Claim    ☐ Other: _____

Notary Service Performed at:

**IDENTIFICATION**
Type:
Number:
Issued By:
Expires:

Notes/Comments:

Witness Name/Address:     Witness Signature:

Known Personally: ☐ Yes ☐ No

**RECORD NUMBER 109**

---

## RECORD NUMBER 110

| Name of Signer (printed) | Signer's Signature | Fee Charged:$ |
|---|---|---|

Signer's FULL Address      Phone No.      Right Thumb Print *(When Applicable)*

Notary Service(s) Performed   ☐ Jurat   ☐ Acknowledgment   ☐ Oath

Other(Details)

Date Notarized:     Time:     AM PM

Document:     Document Date:

☐ Affidavit    ☐ Trust    ☐ Acknowledgement
☐ Mortgage/Deed    ☐ Will    ☐ Power of Attorney
☐ Auto Title    ☐ Claim    ☐ Other: _____

Notary Service Performed at:

**IDENTIFICATION**
Type:
Number:
Issued By:
Expires:

Notes/Comments:

Witness Name/Address:     Witness Signature:

Known Personally: ☐ Yes ☐ No

**RECORD NUMBER 110**

---

## RECORD NUMBER 111

| Name of Signer (printed) | Signer's Signature | Fee Charged:$ |
|---|---|---|

Signer's FULL Address      Phone No.      Right Thumb Print *(When Applicable)*

Notary Service(s) Performed   ☐ Jurat   ☐ Acknowledgment   ☐ Oath

Other(Details)

Date Notarized:     Time:     AM PM

Document:     Document Date:

☐ Affidavit    ☐ Trust    ☐ Acknowledgement
☐ Mortgage/Deed    ☐ Will    ☐ Power of Attorney
☐ Auto Title    ☐ Claim    ☐ Other: _____

Notary Service Performed at:

**IDENTIFICATION**
Type:
Number:
Issued By:
Expires:

Notes/Comments:

Witness Name/Address:     Witness Signature:

Known Personally: ☐ Yes ☐ No

**RECORD NUMBER 111**

| Name of Signer (printed) | Signer's Signature | Fee Charged:$ |
|---|---|---|

| Right Thumb Print (When Applicable) | Signer's FULL Address | Phone No. |
|---|---|---|

| | Notary Service(s) Performed  ☐Jurat  ☐Acknowledgment  ☐Oath | Date Notarized:  Time: |
|---|---|---|
| | Other(Details) | AM PM |

| Notes/Comments: | Document:            Document Date: | **IDENTIFICATION** Type: |
|---|---|---|
| | ☐ Affidavit  ☐ Trust  ☐ Acknowledgement | Number: |
| | ☐ Mortgage/Deed  ☐ Will  ☐ Power of Attorney | |
| | ☐ Auto Title  ☐ Claim  ☐ Other: _____ | Issued By: |
| | Notary Service Performed at: | Expires: |

| RECORD NUMBER **112** | Witness Name/Address:  Witness Signature: | Known Personally:  ☐Yes ☐No |
|---|---|---|

---

| Name of Signer (printed) | Signer's Signature | Fee Charged:$ |
|---|---|---|

| Right Thumb Print (When Applicable) | Signer's FULL Address | Phone No. |
|---|---|---|

| | Notary Service(s) Performed  ☐Jurat  ☐Acknowledgment  ☐Oath | Date Notarized:  Time: |
|---|---|---|
| | Other(Details) | AM PM |

| Notes/Comments: | Document:            Document Date: | **IDENTIFICATION** Type: |
|---|---|---|
| | ☐ Affidavit  ☐ Trust  ☐ Acknowledgement | Number: |
| | ☐ Mortgage/Deed  ☐ Will  ☐ Power of Attorney | |
| | ☐ Auto Title  ☐ Claim  ☐ Other: _____ | Issued By: |
| | Notary Service Performed at: | Expires: |

| RECORD NUMBER **113** | Witness Name/Address:  Witness Signature: | Known Personally:  ☐Yes ☐No |
|---|---|---|

---

| Name of Signer (printed) | Signer's Signature | Fee Charged:$ |
|---|---|---|

| Right Thumb Print (When Applicable) | Signer's FULL Address | Phone No. |
|---|---|---|

| | Notary Service(s) Performed  ☐Jurat  ☐Acknowledgment  ☐Oath | Date Notarized:  Time: |
|---|---|---|
| | Other(Details) | AM PM |

| Notes/Comments: | Document:            Document Date: | **IDENTIFICATION** Type: |
|---|---|---|
| | ☐ Affidavit  ☐ Trust  ☐ Acknowledgement | Number: |
| | ☐ Mortgage/Deed  ☐ Will  ☐ Power of Attorney | |
| | ☐ Auto Title  ☐ Claim  ☐ Other: _____ | Issued By: |
| | Notary Service Performed at: | Expires: |

| RECORD NUMBER **114** | Witness Name/Address:  Witness Signature: | Known Personally:  ☐Yes ☐No |
|---|---|---|

## RECORD NUMBER 115

| Name of Signer (printed) | Signer's Signature | Fee Charged: $ |
|---|---|---|

Signer's FULL Address                    Phone No.

Right Thumb Print *(When Applicable)*

Notary Service(s) Performed   ☐ Jurat   ☐ Acknowledgment   ☐ Oath

Other(Details)

Date Notarized:         Time:

AM  PM

Document:                          Document Date:

**IDENTIFICATION**

Type:

☐ Affidavit      ☐ Trust      ☐ Acknowledgement
☐ Mortgage/Deed  ☐ Will       ☐ Power of Attorney
☐ Auto Title     ☐ Claim      ☐ Other: _____

Number:

Issued By:

Notary Service Performed at:

Expires:

Notes/Comments:

Witness Name/Address:              Witness Signature:

Known Personally:   ☐ Yes   ☐ No

**RECORD NUMBER 115**

---

## RECORD NUMBER 116

| Name of Signer (printed) | Signer's Signature | Fee Charged: $ |
|---|---|---|

Signer's FULL Address                    Phone No.

Right Thumb Print *(When Applicable)*

Notary Service(s) Performed   ☐ Jurat   ☐ Acknowledgment   ☐ Oath

Other(Details)

Date Notarized:         Time:

AM  PM

Document:                          Document Date:

**IDENTIFICATION**

Type:

☐ Affidavit      ☐ Trust      ☐ Acknowledgement
☐ Mortgage/Deed  ☐ Will       ☐ Power of Attorney
☐ Auto Title     ☐ Claim      ☐ Other: _____

Number:

Issued By:

Notary Service Performed at:

Expires:

Notes/Comments:

Witness Name/Address:              Witness Signature:

Known Personally:   ☐ Yes   ☐ No

**RECORD NUMBER 116**

---

## RECORD NUMBER 117

| Name of Signer (printed) | Signer's Signature | Fee Charged: $ |
|---|---|---|

Signer's FULL Address                    Phone No.

Right Thumb Print *(When Applicable)*

Notary Service(s) Performed   ☐ Jurat   ☐ Acknowledgment   ☐ Oath

Other(Details)

Date Notarized:         Time:

AM  PM

Document:                          Document Date:

**IDENTIFICATION**

Type:

☐ Affidavit      ☐ Trust      ☐ Acknowledgement
☐ Mortgage/Deed  ☐ Will       ☐ Power of Attorney
☐ Auto Title     ☐ Claim      ☐ Other: _____

Number:

Issued By:

Notary Service Performed at:

Expires:

Notes/Comments:

Witness Name/Address:              Witness Signature:

Known Personally:   ☐ Yes   ☐ No

**RECORD NUMBER 117**

| Name of Signer *(printed)* | Signer's Signature | Fee Charged:$ |
|---|---|---|

| Right Thumb Print *(When Applicable)* | Signer's FULL Address | Phone No. |
|---|---|---|
| | Notary Service(s) Performed ☐Jurat ☐Acknowledgment ☐Oath<br><br>Other(Details) | Date Notarized: Time:<br><br>AM PM |
| Notes/Comments: | Document: Document Date:<br><br>☐ Affidavit ☐ Trust ☐ Acknowledgement<br>☐ Mortgage/Deed ☐ Will ☐ Power of Attorney<br>☐ Auto Title ☐ Claim ☐ Other: _____<br><br>Notary Service Performed at: | **IDENTIFICATION**<br>Type:<br><br>Number:<br><br>Issued By:<br><br>Expires: |
| **RECORD NUMBER**<br>**118** | Witness Name/Address: Witness Signature: | Known Personally:<br><br>☐Yes ☐No |

| Name of Signer *(printed)* | Signer's Signature | Fee Charged:$ |
|---|---|---|

| Right Thumb Print *(When Applicable)* | Signer's FULL Address | Phone No. |
|---|---|---|
| | Notary Service(s) Performed ☐Jurat ☐Acknowledgment ☐Oath<br><br>Other(Details) | Date Notarized: Time:<br><br>AM PM |
| Notes/Comments: | Document: Document Date:<br><br>☐ Affidavit ☐ Trust ☐ Acknowledgement<br>☐ Mortgage/Deed ☐ Will ☐ Power of Attorney<br>☐ Auto Title ☐ Claim ☐ Other: _____<br><br>Notary Service Performed at: | **IDENTIFICATION**<br>Type:<br><br>Number:<br><br>Issued By:<br><br>Expires: |
| **RECORD NUMBER**<br>**119** | Witness Name/Address: Witness Signature: | Known Personally:<br><br>☐Yes ☐No |

| Name of Signer *(printed)* | Signer's Signature | Fee Charged:$ |
|---|---|---|

| Right Thumb Print *(When Applicable)* | Signer's FULL Address | Phone No. |
|---|---|---|
| | Notary Service(s) Performed ☐Jurat ☐Acknowledgment ☐Oath<br><br>Other(Details) | Date Notarized: Time:<br><br>AM PM |
| Notes/Comments: | Document: Document Date:<br><br>☐ Affidavit ☐ Trust ☐ Acknowledgement<br>☐ Mortgage/Deed ☐ Will ☐ Power of Attorney<br>☐ Auto Title ☐ Claim ☐ Other: _____<br><br>Notary Service Performed at: | **IDENTIFICATION**<br>Type:<br><br>Number:<br><br>Issued By:<br><br>Expires: |
| **RECORD NUMBER**<br>**120** | Witness Name/Address: Witness Signature: | Known Personally:<br><br>☐Yes ☐No |

| Name of Signer (printed) | Signer's Signature | Fee Charged:$ |
|---|---|---|

Signer's FULL Address        Phone No.

**Right Thumb Print** *(When Applicable)*

Notary Service(s) Performed  ☐ Jurat  ☐ Acknowledgment  ☐ Oath

Other(Details)

Date Notarized:     Time:

AM PM

Document:             Document Date:

**IDENTIFICATION**

Type:

☐ Affidavit    ☐ Trust    ☐ Acknowledgement

☐ Mortgage/Deed    ☐ Will    ☐ Power of Attorney

☐ Auto Title    ☐ Claim    ☐ Other: _____

Number:

Issued By:

Notary Service Performed at:

Expires:

Notes/Comments:

Witness Name/Address:        Witness Signature:

Known Personally:

☐ **Yes**  ☐ **No**

**RECORD NUMBER**
**121**

---

| Name of Signer (printed) | Signer's Signature | Fee Charged:$ |
|---|---|---|

Signer's FULL Address        Phone No.

**Right Thumb Print** *(When Applicable)*

Notary Service(s) Performed  ☐ Jurat  ☐ Acknowledgment  ☐ Oath

Other(Details)

Date Notarized:     Time:

AM PM

Document:             Document Date:

**IDENTIFICATION**

Type:

☐ Affidavit    ☐ Trust    ☐ Acknowledgement

☐ Mortgage/Deed    ☐ Will    ☐ Power of Attorney

☐ Auto Title    ☐ Claim    ☐ Other: _____

Number:

Issued By:

Notary Service Performed at:

Expires:

Notes/Comments:

Witness Name/Address:        Witness Signature:

Known Personally:

☐ **Yes**  ☐ **No**

**RECORD NUMBER**
**122**

---

| Name of Signer (printed) | Signer's Signature | Fee Charged:$ |
|---|---|---|

Signer's FULL Address        Phone No.

**Right Thumb Print** *(When Applicable)*

Notary Service(s) Performed  ☐ Jurat  ☐ Acknowledgment  ☐ Oath

Other(Details)

Date Notarized:     Time:

AM PM

Document:             Document Date:

**IDENTIFICATION**

Type:

☐ Affidavit    ☐ Trust    ☐ Acknowledgement

☐ Mortgage/Deed    ☐ Will    ☐ Power of Attorney

☐ Auto Title    ☐ Claim    ☐ Other: _____

Number:

Issued By:

Notary Service Performed at:

Expires:

Notes/Comments:

Witness Name/Address:        Witness Signature:

Known Personally:

☐ **Yes**  ☐ **No**

**RECORD NUMBER**
**123**

| Name of Signer (printed) | Signer's Signature | Fee Charged:$ |
|---|---|---|

| Right Thumb Print (When Applicable) | Signer's FULL Address | Phone No. |
|---|---|---|

**Notary Service(s) Performed** ☐Jurat ☐Acknowledgment ☐Oath

Other(Details)

**Date Notarized:** **Time:**

**AM PM**

**IDENTIFICATION**

Type:

| Notes/Comments: | Document: | Document Date: |
|---|---|---|

☐ Affidavit ☐ Trust ☐ Acknowledgement

☐ Mortgage/Deed ☐ Will ☐ Power of Attorney

☐ Auto Title ☐ Claim ☐ Other: _____

Notary Service Performed at:

Number:

Issued By:

Expires:

**RECORD NUMBER 124**

Witness Name/Address: Witness Signature:

Known Personally:

☐Yes ☐No

---

| Name of Signer (printed) | Signer's Signature | Fee Charged:$ |
|---|---|---|

| Right Thumb Print (When Applicable) | Signer's FULL Address | Phone No. |
|---|---|---|

**Notary Service(s) Performed** ☐Jurat ☐Acknowledgment ☐Oath

Other(Details)

**Date Notarized:** **Time:**

**AM PM**

**IDENTIFICATION**

Type:

| Notes/Comments: | Document: | Document Date: |
|---|---|---|

☐ Affidavit ☐ Trust ☐ Acknowledgement

☐ Mortgage/Deed ☐ Will ☐ Power of Attorney

☐ Auto Title ☐ Claim ☐ Other: _____

Notary Service Performed at:

Number:

Issued By:

Expires:

**RECORD NUMBER 125**

Witness Name/Address: Witness Signature:

Known Personally:

☐Yes ☐No

---

| Name of Signer (printed) | Signer's Signature | Fee Charged:$ |
|---|---|---|

| Right Thumb Print (When Applicable) | Signer's FULL Address | Phone No. |
|---|---|---|

**Notary Service(s) Performed** ☐Jurat ☐Acknowledgment ☐Oath

Other(Details)

**Date Notarized:** **Time:**

**AM PM**

**IDENTIFICATION**

Type:

| Notes/Comments: | Document: | Document Date: |
|---|---|---|

☐ Affidavit ☐ Trust ☐ Acknowledgement

☐ Mortgage/Deed ☐ Will ☐ Power of Attorney

☐ Auto Title ☐ Claim ☐ Other: _____

Notary Service Performed at:

Number:

Issued By:

Expires:

**RECORD NUMBER 126**

Witness Name/Address: Witness Signature:

Known Personally:

☐Yes ☐No

| Name of Signer *(printed)* | Signer's Signature | Fee Charged:$ |
| --- | --- | --- |

| Signer's FULL Address | Phone No. | Right Thumb Print *(When Applicable)* |
| --- | --- | --- |

Notary Service(s) Performed ☐ Jurat ☐ Acknowledgment ☐ Oath

Other(Details)

Date Notarized:     Time:

AM PM

Document:     Document Date:

**IDENTIFICATION**

Type:

☐ Affidavit    ☐ Trust    ☐ Acknowledgement

☐ Mortgage/Deed    ☐ Will    ☐ Power of Attorney

☐ Auto Title    ☐ Claim    ☐ Other: _____

Number:

Issued By:

Notary Service Performed at:

Expires:

Notes/Comments:

Witness Name/Address:     Witness Signature:

Known Personally:    ☐ Yes  ☐ No

**RECORD NUMBER**
**127**

---

| Name of Signer *(printed)* | Signer's Signature | Fee Charged:$ |
| --- | --- | --- |

| Signer's FULL Address | Phone No. | Right Thumb Print *(When Applicable)* |
| --- | --- | --- |

Notary Service(s) Performed ☐ Jurat ☐ Acknowledgment ☐ Oath

Other(Details)

Date Notarized:     Time:

AM PM

Document:     Document Date:

**IDENTIFICATION**

Type:

☐ Affidavit    ☐ Trust    ☐ Acknowledgement

☐ Mortgage/Deed    ☐ Will    ☐ Power of Attorney

☐ Auto Title    ☐ Claim    ☐ Other: _____

Number:

Issued By:

Notary Service Performed at:

Expires:

Notes/Comments:

Witness Name/Address:     Witness Signature:

Known Personally:    ☐ Yes  ☐ No

**RECORD NUMBER**
**128**

---

| Name of Signer *(printed)* | Signer's Signature | Fee Charged:$ |
| --- | --- | --- |

| Signer's FULL Address | Phone No. | Right Thumb Print *(When Applicable)* |
| --- | --- | --- |

Notary Service(s) Performed ☐ Jurat ☐ Acknowledgment ☐ Oath

Other(Details)

Date Notarized:     Time:

AM PM

Document:     Document Date:

**IDENTIFICATION**

Type:

☐ Affidavit    ☐ Trust    ☐ Acknowledgement

☐ Mortgage/Deed    ☐ Will    ☐ Power of Attorney

☐ Auto Title    ☐ Claim    ☐ Other: _____

Number:

Issued By:

Notary Service Performed at:

Expires:

Notes/Comments:

Witness Name/Address:     Witness Signature:

Known Personally:    ☐ Yes  ☐ No

**RECORD NUMBER**
**129**

| Name of Signer (printed) | Signer's Signature | Fee Charged:$ |
|---|---|---|

| Right Thumb Print (When Applicable) | Signer's FULL Address | Phone No. |
|---|---|---|

Notary Service(s) Performed ☐Jurat ☐Acknowledgment ☐Oath

Other(Details)

Date Notarized: Time:

AM PM

| Notes/Comments: | Document: | Document Date: |
|---|---|---|

**IDENTIFICATION**

Type:

☐ Affidavit ☐ Trust ☐ Acknowledgement

☐ Mortgage/Deed ☐ Will ☐ Power of Attorney

☐ Auto Title ☐ Claim ☐ Other: _____

Notary Service Performed at:

Number:

Issued By:

Expires:

| **RECORD NUMBER 130** | Witness Name/Address: | Witness Signature: | Known Personally: ☐Yes ☐No |
|---|---|---|---|

---

| Name of Signer (printed) | Signer's Signature | Fee Charged:$ |
|---|---|---|

| Right Thumb Print (When Applicable) | Signer's FULL Address | Phone No. |
|---|---|---|

Notary Service(s) Performed ☐Jurat ☐Acknowledgment ☐Oath

Other(Details)

Date Notarized: Time:

AM PM

| Notes/Comments: | Document: | Document Date: |
|---|---|---|

**IDENTIFICATION**

Type:

☐ Affidavit ☐ Trust ☐ Acknowledgement

☐ Mortgage/Deed ☐ Will ☐ Power of Attorney

☐ Auto Title ☐ Claim ☐ Other: _____

Notary Service Performed at:

Number:

Issued By:

Expires:

| **RECORD NUMBER 131** | Witness Name/Address: | Witness Signature: | Known Personally: ☐Yes ☐No |
|---|---|---|---|

---

| Name of Signer (printed) | Signer's Signature | Fee Charged:$ |
|---|---|---|

| Right Thumb Print (When Applicable) | Signer's FULL Address | Phone No. |
|---|---|---|

Notary Service(s) Performed ☐Jurat ☐Acknowledgment ☐Oath

Other(Details)

Date Notarized: Time:

AM PM

| Notes/Comments: | Document: | Document Date: |
|---|---|---|

**IDENTIFICATION**

Type:

☐ Affidavit ☐ Trust ☐ Acknowledgement

☐ Mortgage/Deed ☐ Will ☐ Power of Attorney

☐ Auto Title ☐ Claim ☐ Other: _____

Notary Service Performed at:

Number:

Issued By:

Expires:

| **RECORD NUMBER 132** | Witness Name/Address: | Witness Signature: | Known Personally: ☐Yes ☐No |
|---|---|---|---|

## Record 133

| Name of Signer (printed) | Signer's Signature | Fee Charged:$ |
|---|---|---|

Signer's FULL Address — Phone No. — Right Thumb Print *(When Applicable)*

Notary Service(s) Performed   ☐ Jurat   ☐ Acknowledgment   ☐ Oath

Other(Details)

Date Notarized:   Time:   AM   PM

Document:   Document Date:

☐ Affidavit   ☐ Trust   ☐ Acknowledgement
☐ Mortgage/Deed   ☐ Will   ☐ Power of Attorney
☐ Auto Title   ☐ Claim   ☐ Other: _____

Notary Service Performed at:

**IDENTIFICATION**
Type:
Number:
Issued By:
Expires:

Witness Name/Address:   Witness Signature:

Known Personally:   ☐ Yes   ☐ No

Notes/Comments:

**RECORD NUMBER 133**

---

## Record 134

| Name of Signer (printed) | Signer's Signature | Fee Charged:$ |
|---|---|---|

Signer's FULL Address — Phone No. — Right Thumb Print *(When Applicable)*

Notary Service(s) Performed   ☐ Jurat   ☐ Acknowledgment   ☐ Oath

Other(Details)

Date Notarized:   Time:   AM   PM

Document:   Document Date:

☐ Affidavit   ☐ Trust   ☐ Acknowledgement
☐ Mortgage/Deed   ☐ Will   ☐ Power of Attorney
☐ Auto Title   ☐ Claim   ☐ Other: _____

Notary Service Performed at:

**IDENTIFICATION**
Type:
Number:
Issued By:
Expires:

Witness Name/Address:   Witness Signature:

Known Personally:   ☐ Yes   ☐ No

Notes/Comments:

**RECORD NUMBER 134**

---

## Record 135

| Name of Signer (printed) | Signer's Signature | Fee Charged:$ |
|---|---|---|

Signer's FULL Address — Phone No. — Right Thumb Print *(When Applicable)*

Notary Service(s) Performed   ☐ Jurat   ☐ Acknowledgment   ☐ Oath

Other(Details)

Date Notarized:   Time:   AM   PM

Document:   Document Date:

☐ Affidavit   ☐ Trust   ☐ Acknowledgement
☐ Mortgage/Deed   ☐ Will   ☐ Power of Attorney
☐ Auto Title   ☐ Claim   ☐ Other: _____

Notary Service Performed at:

**IDENTIFICATION**
Type:
Number:
Issued By:
Expires:

Witness Name/Address:   Witness Signature:

Known Personally:   ☐ Yes   ☐ No

Notes/Comments:

**RECORD NUMBER 135**

| Name of Signer (printed) | Signer's Signature | Fee Charged:$ |
|---|---|---|

| Right Thumb Print (When Applicable) | Signer's FULL Address | Phone No. |
|---|---|---|
| | Notary Service(s) Performed ☐Jurat ☐Acknowledgment ☐Oath<br>Other(Details) | Date Notarized: Time:<br><br>AM PM |
| Notes/Comments: | Document: Document Date:<br>☐ Affidavit ☐ Trust ☐ Acknowledgement<br>☐ Mortgage/Deed ☐ Will ☐ Power of Attorney<br>☐ Auto Title ☐ Claim ☐ Other: _____<br>Notary Service Performed at: | **IDENTIFICATION**<br>Type:<br>Number:<br>Issued By:<br>Expires: |

**RECORD NUMBER 136**

| Witness Name/Address: | Witness Signature: | Known Personally:<br>☐Yes ☐No |
|---|---|---|

---

| Name of Signer (printed) | Signer's Signature | Fee Charged:$ |
|---|---|---|

| Right Thumb Print (When Applicable) | Signer's FULL Address | Phone No. |
|---|---|---|
| | Notary Service(s) Performed ☐Jurat ☐Acknowledgment ☐Oath<br>Other(Details) | Date Notarized: Time:<br><br>AM PM |
| Notes/Comments: | Document: Document Date:<br>☐ Affidavit ☐ Trust ☐ Acknowledgement<br>☐ Mortgage/Deed ☐ Will ☐ Power of Attorney<br>☐ Auto Title ☐ Claim ☐ Other: _____<br>Notary Service Performed at: | **IDENTIFICATION**<br>Type:<br>Number:<br>Issued By:<br>Expires: |

**RECORD NUMBER 137**

| Witness Name/Address: | Witness Signature: | Known Personally:<br>☐Yes ☐No |
|---|---|---|

---

| Name of Signer (printed) | Signer's Signature | Fee Charged:$ |
|---|---|---|

| Right Thumb Print (When Applicable) | Signer's FULL Address | Phone No. |
|---|---|---|
| | Notary Service(s) Performed ☐Jurat ☐Acknowledgment ☐Oath<br>Other(Details) | Date Notarized: Time:<br><br>AM PM |
| Notes/Comments: | Document: Document Date:<br>☐ Affidavit ☐ Trust ☐ Acknowledgement<br>☐ Mortgage/Deed ☐ Will ☐ Power of Attorney<br>☐ Auto Title ☐ Claim ☐ Other: _____<br>Notary Service Performed at: | **IDENTIFICATION**<br>Type:<br>Number:<br>Issued By:<br>Expires: |

**RECORD NUMBER 138**

| Witness Name/Address: | Witness Signature: | Known Personally:<br>☐Yes ☐No |
|---|---|---|

## Record Number 139

| Name of Signer (printed) | Signer's Signature | Fee Charged: $ |
|---|---|---|

Signer's FULL Address — Phone No. — Right Thumb Print *(When Applicable)*

Notary Service(s) Performed  ☐ Jurat  ☐ Acknowledgment  ☐ Oath

Other(Details)

Date Notarized:   Time:   AM  PM

Document:   Document Date:

☐ Affidavit  ☐ Trust  ☐ Acknowledgement
☐ Mortgage/Deed  ☐ Will  ☐ Power of Attorney
☐ Auto Title  ☐ Claim  ☐ Other: _____

Notary Service Performed at:

**IDENTIFICATION**
Type:
Number:
Issued By:
Expires:

Notes/Comments:

Witness Name/Address:   Witness Signature:

Known Personally:  ☐ Yes  ☐ No

**RECORD NUMBER 139**

---

## Record Number 140

| Name of Signer (printed) | Signer's Signature | Fee Charged: $ |
|---|---|---|

Signer's FULL Address — Phone No. — Right Thumb Print *(When Applicable)*

Notary Service(s) Performed  ☐ Jurat  ☐ Acknowledgment  ☐ Oath

Other(Details)

Date Notarized:   Time:   AM  PM

Document:   Document Date:

☐ Affidavit  ☐ Trust  ☐ Acknowledgement
☐ Mortgage/Deed  ☐ Will  ☐ Power of Attorney
☐ Auto Title  ☐ Claim  ☐ Other: _____

Notary Service Performed at:

**IDENTIFICATION**
Type:
Number:
Issued By:
Expires:

Notes/Comments:

Witness Name/Address:   Witness Signature:

Known Personally:  ☐ Yes  ☐ No

**RECORD NUMBER 140**

---

## Record Number 141

| Name of Signer (printed) | Signer's Signature | Fee Charged: $ |
|---|---|---|

Signer's FULL Address — Phone No. — Right Thumb Print *(When Applicable)*

Notary Service(s) Performed  ☐ Jurat  ☐ Acknowledgment  ☐ Oath

Other(Details)

Date Notarized:   Time:   AM  PM

Document:   Document Date:

☐ Affidavit  ☐ Trust  ☐ Acknowledgement
☐ Mortgage/Deed  ☐ Will  ☐ Power of Attorney
☐ Auto Title  ☐ Claim  ☐ Other: _____

Notary Service Performed at:

**IDENTIFICATION**
Type:
Number:
Issued By:
Expires:

Notes/Comments:

Witness Name/Address:   Witness Signature:

Known Personally:  ☐ Yes  ☐ No

**RECORD NUMBER 141**

| Name of Signer *(printed)* | Signer's Signature | Fee Charged:$ |
|---|---|---|

| Right Thumb Print *(When Applicable)* | Signer's FULL Address | Phone No. |
|---|---|---|

Notary Service(s) Performed  ☐ Jurat  ☐ Acknowledgment  ☐ Oath

Other(Details)

Date Notarized:        Time:

AM  PM

| Notes/Comments: | Document:                                    Document Date: | **IDENTIFICATION** |
|---|---|---|

☐ Affidavit   ☐ Trust   ☐ Acknowledgement
☐ Mortgage/Deed   ☐ Will   ☐ Power of Attorney
☐ Auto Title   ☐ Claim   ☐ Other: _____

Notary Service Performed at:

Type:

Number:

Issued By:

Expires:

**RECORD NUMBER 142**

Witness Name/Address:                    Witness Signature:

Known Personally:
☐ Yes  ☐ No

---

| Name of Signer *(printed)* | Signer's Signature | Fee Charged:$ |
|---|---|---|

| Right Thumb Print *(When Applicable)* | Signer's FULL Address | Phone No. |
|---|---|---|

Notary Service(s) Performed  ☐ Jurat  ☐ Acknowledgment  ☐ Oath

Other(Details)

Date Notarized:        Time:

AM  PM

| Notes/Comments: | Document:                                    Document Date: | **IDENTIFICATION** |
|---|---|---|

☐ Affidavit   ☐ Trust   ☐ Acknowledgement
☐ Mortgage/Deed   ☐ Will   ☐ Power of Attorney
☐ Auto Title   ☐ Claim   ☐ Other: _____

Notary Service Performed at:

Type:

Number:

Issued By:

Expires:

**RECORD NUMBER 143**

Witness Name/Address:                    Witness Signature:

Known Personally:
☐ Yes  ☐ No

---

| Name of Signer *(printed)* | Signer's Signature | Fee Charged:$ |
|---|---|---|

| Right Thumb Print *(When Applicable)* | Signer's FULL Address | Phone No. |
|---|---|---|

Notary Service(s) Performed  ☐ Jurat  ☐ Acknowledgment  ☐ Oath

Other(Details)

Date Notarized:        Time:

AM  PM

| Notes/Comments: | Document:                                    Document Date: | **IDENTIFICATION** |
|---|---|---|

☐ Affidavit   ☐ Trust   ☐ Acknowledgement
☐ Mortgage/Deed   ☐ Will   ☐ Power of Attorney
☐ Auto Title   ☐ Claim   ☐ Other: _____

Notary Service Performed at:

Type:

Number:

Issued By:

Expires:

**RECORD NUMBER 144**

Witness Name/Address:                    Witness Signature:

Known Personally:
☐ Yes  ☐ No

**Name of Signer** *(printed)* | **Signer's Signature** | **Fee Charged:** $

**Signer's FULL Address** | **Phone No.** | **Right Thumb Print** *(When Applicable)*

**Notary Service(s) Performed** ☐ Jurat ☐ Acknowledgment ☐ Oath | **Date Notarized:** **Time:**

**Other(Details)** | AM PM

**Document:** | **Document Date:** | **IDENTIFICATION**

**Type:**

☐ Affidavit ☐ Trust ☐ Acknowledgement

☐ Mortgage/Deed ☐ Will ☐ Power of Attorney | **Number:**

☐ Auto Title ☐ Claim ☐ Other: _____ | **Issued By:**

**Notary Service Performed at:** | **Expires:**

**Witness Name/Address:** | **Witness Signature:** | **Known Personally:** | **Notes/Comments:**

☐ Yes ☐ No | **RECORD NUMBER 145**

---

**Name of Signer** *(printed)* | **Signer's Signature** | **Fee Charged:** $

**Signer's FULL Address** | **Phone No.** | **Right Thumb Print** *(When Applicable)*

**Notary Service(s) Performed** ☐ Jurat ☐ Acknowledgment ☐ Oath | **Date Notarized:** **Time:**

**Other(Details)** | AM PM

**Document:** | **Document Date:** | **IDENTIFICATION**

**Type:**

☐ Affidavit ☐ Trust ☐ Acknowledgement

☐ Mortgage/Deed ☐ Will ☐ Power of Attorney | **Number:**

☐ Auto Title ☐ Claim ☐ Other: _____ | **Issued By:**

**Notary Service Performed at:** | **Expires:**

**Witness Name/Address:** | **Witness Signature:** | **Known Personally:** | **Notes/Comments:**

☐ Yes ☐ No | **RECORD NUMBER 146**

---

**Name of Signer** *(printed)* | **Signer's Signature** | **Fee Charged:** $

**Signer's FULL Address** | **Phone No.** | **Right Thumb Print** *(When Applicable)*

**Notary Service(s) Performed** ☐ Jurat ☐ Acknowledgment ☐ Oath | **Date Notarized:** **Time:**

**Other(Details)** | AM PM

**Document:** | **Document Date:** | **IDENTIFICATION**

**Type:**

☐ Affidavit ☐ Trust ☐ Acknowledgement

☐ Mortgage/Deed ☐ Will ☐ Power of Attorney | **Number:**

☐ Auto Title ☐ Claim ☐ Other: _____ | **Issued By:**

**Notary Service Performed at:** | **Expires:**

**Witness Name/Address:** | **Witness Signature:** | **Known Personally:** | **Notes/Comments:**

☐ Yes ☐ No | **RECORD NUMBER 147**

| Name of Signer (printed) | Signer's Signature | Fee Charged:$ |
|---|---|---|

**Right Thumb Print** (When Applicable)

Signer's FULL Address · Phone No.

| Notary Service(s) Performed | ☐ Jurat | ☐ Acknowledgment | ☐ Oath | Date Notarized: | Time: |

Other(Details)

AM PM

Notes/Comments:

Document: · Document Date:

**IDENTIFICATION**
Type:

☐ Affidavit  ☐ Trust  ☐ Acknowledgement
☐ Mortgage/Deed  ☐ Will  ☐ Power of Attorney
☐ Auto Title  ☐ Claim  ☐ Other: _____

Number:

Issued By:

Notary Service Performed at:

Expires:

**RECORD NUMBER 148**

Witness Name/Address: · Witness Signature:

Known Personally:
☐ Yes ☐ No

---

| Name of Signer (printed) | Signer's Signature | Fee Charged:$ |
|---|---|---|

**Right Thumb Print** (When Applicable)

Signer's FULL Address · Phone No.

| Notary Service(s) Performed | ☐ Jurat | ☐ Acknowledgment | ☐ Oath | Date Notarized: | Time: |

Other(Details)

AM PM

Notes/Comments:

Document: · Document Date:

**IDENTIFICATION**
Type:

☐ Affidavit  ☐ Trust  ☐ Acknowledgement
☐ Mortgage/Deed  ☐ Will  ☐ Power of Attorney
☐ Auto Title  ☐ Claim  ☐ Other: _____

Number:

Issued By:

Notary Service Performed at:

Expires:

**RECORD NUMBER 149**

Witness Name/Address: · Witness Signature:

Known Personally:
☐ Yes ☐ No

---

| Name of Signer (printed) | Signer's Signature | Fee Charged:$ |
|---|---|---|

**Right Thumb Print** (When Applicable)

Signer's FULL Address · Phone No.

| Notary Service(s) Performed | ☐ Jurat | ☐ Acknowledgment | ☐ Oath | Date Notarized: | Time: |

Other(Details)

AM PM

Notes/Comments:

Document: · Document Date:

**IDENTIFICATION**
Type:

☐ Affidavit  ☐ Trust  ☐ Acknowledgement
☐ Mortgage/Deed  ☐ Will  ☐ Power of Attorney
☐ Auto Title  ☐ Claim  ☐ Other: _____

Number:

Issued By:

Notary Service Performed at:

Expires:

**RECORD NUMBER 150**

Witness Name/Address: · Witness Signature:

Known Personally:
☐ Yes ☐ No

| Name of Signer *(printed)* | Signer's Signature | Fee Charged:$ |
|---|---|---|

Signer's FULL Address                     Phone No.

**Right Thumb Print** *(When Applicable)*

Notary Service(s) Performed  ☐ Jurat  ☐ Acknowledgment  ☐ Oath

Other(Details)

Date Notarized:          Time:

AM  PM

Document:                        Document Date:

**IDENTIFICATION**

Type:

☐ Affidavit      ☐ Trust      ☐ Acknowledgement

☐ Mortgage/Deed  ☐ Will       ☐ Power of Attorney

☐ Auto Title     ☐ Claim      ☐ Other: _____

Notary Service Performed at:

Number:

Issued By:

Expires:

Notes/Comments:

Witness Name/Address:              Witness Signature:

Known Personally:

☐ Yes   ☐ No

**RECORD NUMBER**
**151**

---

| Name of Signer *(printed)* | Signer's Signature | Fee Charged:$ |
|---|---|---|

Signer's FULL Address                     Phone No.

**Right Thumb Print** *(When Applicable)*

Notary Service(s) Performed  ☐ Jurat  ☐ Acknowledgment  ☐ Oath

Other(Details)

Date Notarized:          Time:

AM  PM

Document:                        Document Date:

**IDENTIFICATION**

Type:

☐ Affidavit      ☐ Trust      ☐ Acknowledgement

☐ Mortgage/Deed  ☐ Will       ☐ Power of Attorney

☐ Auto Title     ☐ Claim      ☐ Other: _____

Notary Service Performed at:

Number:

Issued By:

Expires:

Notes/Comments:

Witness Name/Address:              Witness Signature:

Known Personally:

☐ Yes   ☐ No

**RECORD NUMBER**
**152**

---

| Name of Signer *(printed)* | Signer's Signature | Fee Charged:$ |
|---|---|---|

Signer's FULL Address                     Phone No.

**Right Thumb Print** *(When Applicable)*

Notary Service(s) Performed  ☐ Jurat  ☐ Acknowledgment  ☐ Oath

Other(Details)

Date Notarized:          Time:

AM  PM

Document:                        Document Date:

**IDENTIFICATION**

Type:

☐ Affidavit      ☐ Trust      ☐ Acknowledgement

☐ Mortgage/Deed  ☐ Will       ☐ Power of Attorney

☐ Auto Title     ☐ Claim      ☐ Other: _____

Notary Service Performed at:

Number:

Issued By:

Expires:

Notes/Comments:

Witness Name/Address:              Witness Signature:

Known Personally:

☐ Yes   ☐ No

**RECORD NUMBER**
**153**

| Name of Signer (printed) | Signer's Signature | Fee Charged:$ |
|---|---|---|

| Right Thumb Print (When Applicable) | Signer's FULL Address | Phone No. |
|---|---|---|
| | Notary Service(s) Performed ☐Jurat ☐Acknowledgment ☐Oath<br>Other(Details) | Date Notarized: Time:<br><br>AM PM |

**IDENTIFICATION**

| Notes/Comments: | Document: Document Date:<br>☐ Affidavit ☐ Trust ☐ Acknowledgement<br>☐ Mortgage/Deed ☐ Will ☐ Power of Attorney<br>☐ Auto Title ☐ Claim ☐ Other: _____<br>Notary Service Performed at: | Type:<br>Number:<br>Issued By:<br>Expires: |
|---|---|---|

**RECORD NUMBER 154**

| Witness Name/Address: | Witness Signature: | Known Personally:<br>☐Yes ☐No |
|---|---|---|

---

| Name of Signer (printed) | Signer's Signature | Fee Charged:$ |
|---|---|---|

| Right Thumb Print (When Applicable) | Signer's FULL Address | Phone No. |
|---|---|---|
| | Notary Service(s) Performed ☐Jurat ☐Acknowledgment ☐Oath<br>Other(Details) | Date Notarized: Time:<br><br>AM PM |

**IDENTIFICATION**

| Notes/Comments: | Document: Document Date:<br>☐ Affidavit ☐ Trust ☐ Acknowledgement<br>☐ Mortgage/Deed ☐ Will ☐ Power of Attorney<br>☐ Auto Title ☐ Claim ☐ Other: _____<br>Notary Service Performed at: | Type:<br>Number:<br>Issued By:<br>Expires: |
|---|---|---|

**RECORD NUMBER 155**

| Witness Name/Address: | Witness Signature: | Known Personally:<br>☐Yes ☐No |
|---|---|---|

---

| Name of Signer (printed) | Signer's Signature | Fee Charged:$ |
|---|---|---|

| Right Thumb Print (When Applicable) | Signer's FULL Address | Phone No. |
|---|---|---|
| | Notary Service(s) Performed ☐Jurat ☐Acknowledgment ☐Oath<br>Other(Details) | Date Notarized: Time:<br><br>AM PM |

**IDENTIFICATION**

| Notes/Comments: | Document: Document Date:<br>☐ Affidavit ☐ Trust ☐ Acknowledgement<br>☐ Mortgage/Deed ☐ Will ☐ Power of Attorney<br>☐ Auto Title ☐ Claim ☐ Other: _____<br>Notary Service Performed at: | Type:<br>Number:<br>Issued By:<br>Expires: |
|---|---|---|

**RECORD NUMBER 156**

| Witness Name/Address: | Witness Signature: | Known Personally:<br>☐Yes ☐No |
|---|---|---|

| Name of Signer *(printed)* | Signer's Signature | Fee Charged: $ |
|---|---|---|

**Signer's FULL Address**  Phone No.

Right Thumb Print *(When Applicable)*

Notary Service(s) Performed  ☐ Jurat  ☐ Acknowledgment  ☐ Oath

Other(Details)

Date Notarized:  Time:

AM PM

**Document:**  Document Date:

☐ Affidavit  ☐ Trust  ☐ Acknowledgement
☐ Mortgage/Deed  ☐ Will  ☐ Power of Attorney
☐ Auto Title  ☐ Claim  ☐ Other: _____

Notary Service Performed at:

**IDENTIFICATION**
Type:
Number:
Issued By:
Expires:

Notes/Comments:

Witness Name/Address:  Witness Signature:

Known Personally:  ☐ Yes  ☐ No

**RECORD NUMBER**
**157**

---

| Name of Signer *(printed)* | Signer's Signature | Fee Charged: $ |
|---|---|---|

**Signer's FULL Address**  Phone No.

Right Thumb Print *(When Applicable)*

Notary Service(s) Performed  ☐ Jurat  ☐ Acknowledgment  ☐ Oath

Other(Details)

Date Notarized:  Time:

AM PM

**Document:**  Document Date:

☐ Affidavit  ☐ Trust  ☐ Acknowledgement
☐ Mortgage/Deed  ☐ Will  ☐ Power of Attorney
☐ Auto Title  ☐ Claim  ☐ Other: _____

Notary Service Performed at:

**IDENTIFICATION**
Type:
Number:
Issued By:
Expires:

Notes/Comments:

Witness Name/Address:  Witness Signature:

Known Personally:  ☐ Yes  ☐ No

**RECORD NUMBER**
**158**

---

| Name of Signer *(printed)* | Signer's Signature | Fee Charged: $ |
|---|---|---|

**Signer's FULL Address**  Phone No.

Right Thumb Print *(When Applicable)*

Notary Service(s) Performed  ☐ Jurat  ☐ Acknowledgment  ☐ Oath

Other(Details)

Date Notarized:  Time:

AM PM

**Document:**  Document Date:

☐ Affidavit  ☐ Trust  ☐ Acknowledgement
☐ Mortgage/Deed  ☐ Will  ☐ Power of Attorney
☐ Auto Title  ☐ Claim  ☐ Other: _____

Notary Service Performed at:

**IDENTIFICATION**
Type:
Number:
Issued By:
Expires:

Notes/Comments:

Witness Name/Address:  Witness Signature:

Known Personally:  ☐ Yes  ☐ No

**RECORD NUMBER**
**159**

| Name of Signer (printed) | Signer's Signature | Fee Charged:$ |
|---|---|---|

**Right Thumb Print** (When Applicable)

Signer's FULL Address — Phone No.

Notary Service(s) Performed ☐ Jurat ☐ Acknowledgment ☐ Oath

Other(Details)

Date Notarized: Time:

AM PM

Notes/Comments:

Document: Document Date:

☐ Affidavit ☐ Trust ☐ Acknowledgement
☐ Mortgage/Deed ☐ Will ☐ Power of Attorney
☐ Auto Title ☐ Claim ☐ Other: _____

Notary Service Performed at:

**IDENTIFICATION**
Type:

Number:

Issued By:

Expires:

**RECORD NUMBER 160**

Witness Name/Address: Witness Signature:

Known Personally:

☐ Yes ☐ No

---

| Name of Signer (printed) | Signer's Signature | Fee Charged:$ |
|---|---|---|

**Right Thumb Print** (When Applicable)

Signer's FULL Address — Phone No.

Notary Service(s) Performed ☐ Jurat ☐ Acknowledgment ☐ Oath

Other(Details)

Date Notarized: Time:

AM PM

Notes/Comments:

Document: Document Date:

☐ Affidavit ☐ Trust ☐ Acknowledgement
☐ Mortgage/Deed ☐ Will ☐ Power of Attorney
☐ Auto Title ☐ Claim ☐ Other: _____

Notary Service Performed at:

**IDENTIFICATION**
Type:

Number:

Issued By:

Expires:

**RECORD NUMBER 161**

Witness Name/Address: Witness Signature:

Known Personally:

☐ Yes ☐ No

---

| Name of Signer (printed) | Signer's Signature | Fee Charged:$ |
|---|---|---|

**Right Thumb Print** (When Applicable)

Signer's FULL Address — Phone No.

Notary Service(s) Performed ☐ Jurat ☐ Acknowledgment ☐ Oath

Other(Details)

Date Notarized: Time:

AM PM

Notes/Comments:

Document: Document Date:

☐ Affidavit ☐ Trust ☐ Acknowledgement
☐ Mortgage/Deed ☐ Will ☐ Power of Attorney
☐ Auto Title ☐ Claim ☐ Other: _____

Notary Service Performed at:

**IDENTIFICATION**
Type:

Number:

Issued By:

Expires:

**RECORD NUMBER 162**

Witness Name/Address: Witness Signature:

Known Personally:

☐ Yes ☐ No

## Record 163

Name of Signer (printed) | Signer's Signature | Fee Charged:$

gner's FULL Address | Phone No. | Right Thumb Print (When Applicable)

tary Service(s) Performed ☐ Jurat ☐ Acknowledgment ☐ Oath | Date Notarized: Time:

her(Details) | AM PM

**IDENTIFICATION**

cument: Document Date: | Type:

☐ Affidavit ☐ Trust ☐ Acknowledgement | Number:

☐ Mortgage/Deed ☐ Will ☐ Power of Attorney | Notes/Comments:

☐ Auto Title ☐ Claim ☐ Other: _____ | Issued By:

otary Service Performed at: | Expires:

tness Name/Address: Witness Signature: | Known Personally: ☐ Yes ☐ No | **RECORD NUMBER 163**

## Record 164

Name of Signer (printed) | Signer's Signature | Fee Charged:$

gner's FULL Address | Phone No. | Right Thumb Print (When Applicable)

tary Service(s) Performed ☐ Jurat ☐ Acknowledgment ☐ Oath | Date Notarized: Time:

her(Details) | AM PM

**IDENTIFICATION**

cument: Document Date: | Type:

☐ Affidavit ☐ Trust ☐ Acknowledgement | Number:

☐ Mortgage/Deed ☐ Will ☐ Power of Attorney | Notes/Comments:

☐ Auto Title ☐ Claim ☐ Other: _____ | Issued By:

otary Service Performed at: | Expires:

tness Name/Address: Witness Signature: | Known Personally: ☐ Yes ☐ No | **RECORD NUMBER 164**

## Record 165

Name of Signer (printed) | Signer's Signature | Fee Charged:$

gner's FULL Address | Phone No. | Right Thumb Print (When Applicable)

tary Service(s) Performed ☐ Jurat ☐ Acknowledgment ☐ Oath | Date Notarized: Time:

her(Details) | AM PM

**IDENTIFICATION**

cument: Document Date: | Type:

☐ Affidavit ☐ Trust ☐ Acknowledgement | Number:

☐ Mortgage/Deed ☐ Will ☐ Power of Attorney | Notes/Comments:

☐ Auto Title ☐ Claim ☐ Other: _____ | Issued By:

otary Service Performed at: | Expires:

tness Name/Address: Witness Signature: | Known Personally: ☐ Yes ☐ No | **RECORD NUMBER 165**

| Name of Signer (printed) | Signer's Signature | Fee Charged: $ |
|---|---|---|

| Right Thumb Print (When Applicable) | Signer's FULL Address | Phone No. |
|---|---|---|

Notary Service(s) Performed ☐ Jurat ☐ Acknowledgment ☐ Oath

Other(Details)

Date Notarized:     Time:

AM PM

**IDENTIFICATION**

| Notes/Comments: | Document:                    Document Date: | Type: |
|---|---|---|

☐ Affidavit ☐ Trust ☐ Acknowledgement

☐ Mortgage/Deed ☐ Will ☐ Power of Attorney

☐ Auto Title ☐ Claim ☐ Other: _____

Notary Service Performed at:

Number:

Issued By:

Expires:

**RECORD NUMBER 166**

Witness Name/Address:          Witness Signature:

Known Personally:

☐ Yes ☐ No

---

| Name of Signer (printed) | Signer's Signature | Fee Charged: $ |
|---|---|---|

| Right Thumb Print (When Applicable) | Signer's FULL Address | Phone No. |
|---|---|---|

Notary Service(s) Performed ☐ Jurat ☐ Acknowledgment ☐ Oath

Other(Details)

Date Notarized:     Time:

AM PM

**IDENTIFICATION**

| Notes/Comments: | Document:                    Document Date: | Type: |
|---|---|---|

☐ Affidavit ☐ Trust ☐ Acknowledgement

☐ Mortgage/Deed ☐ Will ☐ Power of Attorney

☐ Auto Title ☐ Claim ☐ Other: _____

Notary Service Performed at:

Number:

Issued By:

Expires:

**RECORD NUMBER 167**

Witness Name/Address:          Witness Signature:

Known Personally:

☐ Yes ☐ No

---

| Name of Signer (printed) | Signer's Signature | Fee Charged: $ |
|---|---|---|

| Right Thumb Print (When Applicable) | Signer's FULL Address | Phone No. |
|---|---|---|

Notary Service(s) Performed ☐ Jurat ☐ Acknowledgment ☐ Oath

Other(Details)

Date Notarized:     Time:

AM PM

**IDENTIFICATION**

| Notes/Comments: | Document:                    Document Date: | Type: |
|---|---|---|

☐ Affidavit ☐ Trust ☐ Acknowledgement

☐ Mortgage/Deed ☐ Will ☐ Power of Attorney

☐ Auto Title ☐ Claim ☐ Other: _____

Notary Service Performed at:

Number:

Issued By:

Expires:

**RECORD NUMBER 168**

Witness Name/Address:          Witness Signature:

Known Personally:

☐ Yes ☐ No

| Name of Signer (printed) | Signer's Signature | Fee Charged:$ |
|---|---|---|

**Signer's FULL Address**      Phone No.     Right Thumb Print *(When Applicable)*

Notary Service(s) Performed  ☐ Jurat  ☐ Acknowledgment  ☐ Oath  Date Notarized:  Time:

Other(Details)      AM PM

**Document:**    Document Date:  **IDENTIFICATION**  Notes/Comments:

Type:

☐ Affidavit  ☐ Trust  ☐ Acknowledgement

☐ Mortgage/Deed  ☐ Will  ☐ Power of Attorney  Number:

☐ Auto Title  ☐ Claim  ☐ Other: _____  Issued By:

Notary Service Performed at:  Expires:

Witness Name/Address:  Witness Signature:  Known Personally:  **RECORD NUMBER**

☐ Yes ☐ No  **169**

---

| Name of Signer (printed) | Signer's Signature | Fee Charged:$ |
|---|---|---|

**Signer's FULL Address**      Phone No.     Right Thumb Print *(When Applicable)*

Notary Service(s) Performed  ☐ Jurat  ☐ Acknowledgment  ☐ Oath  Date Notarized:  Time:

Other(Details)      AM PM

**Document:**    Document Date:  **IDENTIFICATION**  Notes/Comments:

Type:

☐ Affidavit  ☐ Trust  ☐ Acknowledgement

☐ Mortgage/Deed  ☐ Will  ☐ Power of Attorney  Number:

☐ Auto Title  ☐ Claim  ☐ Other: _____  Issued By:

Notary Service Performed at:  Expires:

Witness Name/Address:  Witness Signature:  Known Personally:  **RECORD NUMBER**

☐ Yes ☐ No  **170**

---

| Name of Signer (printed) | Signer's Signature | Fee Charged:$ |
|---|---|---|

**Signer's FULL Address**      Phone No.     Right Thumb Print *(When Applicable)*

Notary Service(s) Performed  ☐ Jurat  ☐ Acknowledgment  ☐ Oath  Date Notarized:  Time:

Other(Details)      AM PM

**Document:**    Document Date:  **IDENTIFICATION**  Notes/Comments:

Type:

☐ Affidavit  ☐ Trust  ☐ Acknowledgement

☐ Mortgage/Deed  ☐ Will  ☐ Power of Attorney  Number:

☐ Auto Title  ☐ Claim  ☐ Other: _____  Issued By:

Notary Service Performed at:  Expires:

Witness Name/Address:  Witness Signature:  Known Personally:  **RECORD NUMBER**

☐ Yes ☐ No  **171**

| Name of Signer *(printed)* | Signer's Signature | Fee Charged:$ |
|---|---|---|

| Right Thumb Print *(When Applicable)* | Signer's FULL Address | Phone No. |
|---|---|---|

Notary Service(s) Performed   ☐ Jurat   ☐ Acknowledgment   ☐ Oath

Other(Details)

| Notes/Comments: | Document: | Document Date: | **IDENTIFICATION** |
|---|---|---|---|

Type:

☐ Affidavit   ☐ Trust   ☐ Acknowledgement

Number:

☐ Mortgage/Deed   ☐ Will   ☐ Power of Attorney

Issued By:

☐ Auto Title   ☐ Claim   ☐ Other: _____

Expires:

Notary Service Performed at:

| **RECORD NUMBER 172** | Witness Name/Address: | Witness Signature: | Known Personally: ☐ Yes ☐ No |
|---|---|---|---|

---

| Name of Signer *(printed)* | Signer's Signature | Fee Charged:$ |
|---|---|---|

| Right Thumb Print *(When Applicable)* | Signer's FULL Address | Phone No. |
|---|---|---|

Notary Service(s) Performed   ☐ Jurat   ☐ Acknowledgment   ☐ Oath

Other(Details)

| Notes/Comments: | Document: | Document Date: | **IDENTIFICATION** |
|---|---|---|---|

Type:

☐ Affidavit   ☐ Trust   ☐ Acknowledgement

Number:

☐ Mortgage/Deed   ☐ Will   ☐ Power of Attorney

Issued By:

☐ Auto Title   ☐ Claim   ☐ Other: _____

Expires:

Notary Service Performed at:

| **RECORD NUMBER 173** | Witness Name/Address: | Witness Signature: | Known Personally: ☐ Yes ☐ No |
|---|---|---|---|

---

| Name of Signer *(printed)* | Signer's Signature | Fee Charged:$ |
|---|---|---|

| Right Thumb Print *(When Applicable)* | Signer's FULL Address | Phone No. |
|---|---|---|

Notary Service(s) Performed   ☐ Jurat   ☐ Acknowledgment   ☐ Oath

Other(Details)

| Notes/Comments: | Document: | Document Date: | **IDENTIFICATION** |
|---|---|---|---|

Type:

☐ Affidavit   ☐ Trust   ☐ Acknowledgement

Number:

☐ Mortgage/Deed   ☐ Will   ☐ Power of Attorney

Issued By:

☐ Auto Title   ☐ Claim   ☐ Other: _____

Expires:

Notary Service Performed at:

| **RECORD NUMBER 174** | Witness Name/Address: | Witness Signature: | Known Personally: ☐ Yes ☐ No |
|---|---|---|---|

**Name of Signer** *(printed)*　　　　　　**Signer's Signature**　　　　　　**Fee Charged:** $

**Signer's FULL Address**　　　　　　　　　　　　Phone No.　　　**Right Thumb Print** *(When Applicable)*

**Notary Service(s) Performed**　☐ Jurat　☐ Acknowledgment　☐ Oath　　**Date Notarized:**　　**Time:**

Other(Details)

　　　　　　　　　　　　　　　　　　　　　　　　　　　　　　　　AM　PM

**Document:**　　　　　　　　　　　**Document Date:**　　**IDENTIFICATION**　　Notes/Comments:

Type:

☐ Affidavit　　☐ Trust　　☐ Acknowledgement

☐ Mortgage/Deed　☐ Will　☐ Power of Attorney　　Number:

☐ Auto Title　　☐ Claim　☐ Other: _____　Issued By:

Notary Service Performed at:

Expires:

**Witness Name/Address:**　　　**Witness Signature:**　　Known Personally:　　**RECORD NUMBER**

☐ Yes　☐ No　　**175**

---

**Name of Signer** *(printed)*　　　　　　**Signer's Signature**　　　　　　**Fee Charged:** $

**Signer's FULL Address**　　　　　　　　　　　　Phone No.　　　**Right Thumb Print** *(When Applicable)*

**Notary Service(s) Performed**　☐ Jurat　☐ Acknowledgment　☐ Oath　　**Date Notarized:**　　**Time:**

Other(Details)

　　　　　　　　　　　　　　　　　　　　　　　　　　　　　　　　AM　PM

**Document:**　　　　　　　　　　　**Document Date:**　　**IDENTIFICATION**　　Notes/Comments:

Type:

☐ Affidavit　　☐ Trust　　☐ Acknowledgement

☐ Mortgage/Deed　☐ Will　☐ Power of Attorney　　Number:

☐ Auto Title　　☐ Claim　☐ Other: _____　Issued By:

Notary Service Performed at:

Expires:

**Witness Name/Address:**　　　**Witness Signature:**　　Known Personally:　　**RECORD NUMBER**

☐ Yes　☐ No　　**176**

---

**Name of Signer** *(printed)*　　　　　　**Signer's Signature**　　　　　　**Fee Charged:** $

**Signer's FULL Address**　　　　　　　　　　　　Phone No.　　　**Right Thumb Print** *(When Applicable)*

**Notary Service(s) Performed**　☐ Jurat　☐ Acknowledgment　☐ Oath　　**Date Notarized:**　　**Time:**

Other(Details)

　　　　　　　　　　　　　　　　　　　　　　　　　　　　　　　　AM　PM

**Document:**　　　　　　　　　　　**Document Date:**　　**IDENTIFICATION**　　Notes/Comments:

Type:

☐ Affidavit　　☐ Trust　　☐ Acknowledgement

☐ Mortgage/Deed　☐ Will　☐ Power of Attorney　　Number:

☐ Auto Title　　☐ Claim　☐ Other: _____　Issued By:

Notary Service Performed at:

Expires:

**Witness Name/Address:**　　　**Witness Signature:**　　Known Personally:　　**RECORD NUMBER**

☐ Yes　☐ No　　**177**

## RECORD NUMBER 178

| Name of Signer (printed) | Signer's Signature | Fee Charged: $ |
|---|---|---|

**Right Thumb Print** (When Applicable)

Signer's FULL Address

Phone No.

Notary Service(s) Performed  ☐ Jurat  ☐ Acknowledgment  ☐ Oath

Other(Details)

Date Notarized:  Time:

AM  PM

**IDENTIFICATION**

Notes/Comments:

Document:  Document Date:

☐ Affidavit  ☐ Trust  ☐ Acknowledgement
☐ Mortgage/Deed  ☐ Will  ☐ Power of Attorney
☐ Auto Title  ☐ Claim  ☐ Other: _____

Notary Service Performed at:

Type:

Number:

Issued By:

Expires:

Witness Name/Address:  Witness Signature:

Known Personally:
☐ Yes  ☐ No

---

## RECORD NUMBER 179

| Name of Signer (printed) | Signer's Signature | Fee Charged: $ |
|---|---|---|

**Right Thumb Print** (When Applicable)

Signer's FULL Address

Phone No.

Notary Service(s) Performed  ☐ Jurat  ☐ Acknowledgment  ☐ Oath

Other(Details)

Date Notarized:  Time:

AM  PM

**IDENTIFICATION**

Notes/Comments:

Document:  Document Date:

☐ Affidavit  ☐ Trust  ☐ Acknowledgement
☐ Mortgage/Deed  ☐ Will  ☐ Power of Attorney
☐ Auto Title  ☐ Claim  ☐ Other: _____

Notary Service Performed at:

Type:

Number:

Issued By:

Expires:

Witness Name/Address:  Witness Signature:

Known Personally:
☐ Yes  ☐ No

---

## RECORD NUMBER 180

| Name of Signer (printed) | Signer's Signature | Fee Charged: $ |
|---|---|---|

**Right Thumb Print** (When Applicable)

Signer's FULL Address

Phone No.

Notary Service(s) Performed  ☐ Jurat  ☐ Acknowledgment  ☐ Oath

Other(Details)

Date Notarized:  Time:

AM  PM

**IDENTIFICATION**

Notes/Comments:

Document:  Document Date:

☐ Affidavit  ☐ Trust  ☐ Acknowledgement
☐ Mortgage/Deed  ☐ Will  ☐ Power of Attorney
☐ Auto Title  ☐ Claim  ☐ Other: _____

Notary Service Performed at:

Type:

Number:

Issued By:

Expires:

Witness Name/Address:  Witness Signature:

Known Personally:
☐ Yes  ☐ No

## Record 181

| Name of Signer (printed) | Signer's Signature | Fee Charged: $ |
|---|---|---|

Signer's FULL Address — Phone No. — Right Thumb Print *(When Applicable)*

Notary Service(s) Performed  ☐ Jurat  ☐ Acknowledgment  ☐ Oath

Other(Details)

Date Notarized: — Time: — AM PM

Document: — Document Date:

☐ Affidavit  ☐ Trust  ☐ Acknowledgement
☐ Mortgage/Deed  ☐ Will  ☐ Power of Attorney
☐ Auto Title  ☐ Claim  ☐ Other: _____

Notary Service Performed at:

Witness Name/Address:  Witness Signature:

**IDENTIFICATION**
Type:
Number:
Issued By:
Expires:
Known Personally:  ☐ Yes  ☐ No

Notes/Comments:

**RECORD NUMBER 181**

## Record 182

| Name of Signer (printed) | Signer's Signature | Fee Charged: $ |
|---|---|---|

Signer's FULL Address — Phone No. — Right Thumb Print *(When Applicable)*

Notary Service(s) Performed  ☐ Jurat  ☐ Acknowledgment  ☐ Oath

Other(Details)

Date Notarized: — Time: — AM PM

Document: — Document Date:

☐ Affidavit  ☐ Trust  ☐ Acknowledgement
☐ Mortgage/Deed  ☐ Will  ☐ Power of Attorney
☐ Auto Title  ☐ Claim  ☐ Other: _____

Notary Service Performed at:

Witness Name/Address:  Witness Signature:

**IDENTIFICATION**
Type:
Number:
Issued By:
Expires:
Known Personally:  ☐ Yes  ☐ No

Notes/Comments:

**RECORD NUMBER 182**

## Record 183

| Name of Signer (printed) | Signer's Signature | Fee Charged: $ |
|---|---|---|

Signer's FULL Address — Phone No. — Right Thumb Print *(When Applicable)*

Notary Service(s) Performed  ☐ Jurat  ☐ Acknowledgment  ☐ Oath

Other(Details)

Date Notarized: — Time: — AM PM

Document: — Document Date:

☐ Affidavit  ☐ Trust  ☐ Acknowledgement
☐ Mortgage/Deed  ☐ Will  ☐ Power of Attorney
☐ Auto Title  ☐ Claim  ☐ Other: _____

Notary Service Performed at:

Witness Name/Address:  Witness Signature:

**IDENTIFICATION**
Type:
Number:
Issued By:
Expires:
Known Personally:  ☐ Yes  ☐ No

Notes/Comments:

**RECORD NUMBER 183**

| Name of Signer *(printed)* | Signer's Signature | Fee Charged:$ |
|---|---|---|

| Right Thumb Print *(When Applicable)* | Signer's FULL Address | Phone No. |
|---|---|---|

**Notary Service(s) Performed** ☐ Jurat ☐ Acknowledgment ☐ Oath

Other(Details)

**Date Notarized:** **Time:**

**AM PM**

**IDENTIFICATION**

Document: Document Date:

Type:

☐ Affidavit ☐ Trust ☐ Acknowledgement

Number:

☐ Mortgage/Deed ☐ Will ☐ Power of Attorney

Issued By:

☐ Auto Title ☐ Claim ☐ Other: _____

Notary Service Performed at:

Expires:

Notes/Comments:

Witness Name/Address: Witness Signature:

Known Personally:

**RECORD NUMBER 184**

☐ Yes ☐ No

---

| Name of Signer *(printed)* | Signer's Signature | Fee Charged:$ |
|---|---|---|

| Right Thumb Print *(When Applicable)* | Signer's FULL Address | Phone No. |
|---|---|---|

**Notary Service(s) Performed** ☐ Jurat ☐ Acknowledgment ☐ Oath

Other(Details)

**Date Notarized:** **Time:**

**AM PM**

**IDENTIFICATION**

Document: Document Date:

Type:

☐ Affidavit ☐ Trust ☐ Acknowledgement

Number:

☐ Mortgage/Deed ☐ Will ☐ Power of Attorney

Issued By:

☐ Auto Title ☐ Claim ☐ Other: _____

Notary Service Performed at:

Expires:

Notes/Comments:

Witness Name/Address: Witness Signature:

Known Personally:

**RECORD NUMBER 185**

☐ Yes ☐ No

---

| Name of Signer *(printed)* | Signer's Signature | Fee Charged:$ |
|---|---|---|

| Right Thumb Print *(When Applicable)* | Signer's FULL Address | Phone No. |
|---|---|---|

**Notary Service(s) Performed** ☐ Jurat ☐ Acknowledgment ☐ Oath

Other(Details)

**Date Notarized:** **Time:**

**AM PM**

**IDENTIFICATION**

Document: Document Date:

Type:

☐ Affidavit ☐ Trust ☐ Acknowledgement

Number:

☐ Mortgage/Deed ☐ Will ☐ Power of Attorney

Issued By:

☐ Auto Title ☐ Claim ☐ Other: _____

Notary Service Performed at:

Expires:

Notes/Comments:

Witness Name/Address: Witness Signature:

Known Personally:

**RECORD NUMBER 186**

☐ Yes ☐ No

**Name of Signer** (printed) | **Signer's Signature** | **Fee Charged:** $

**Signer's FULL Address** | Phone No. | **Right Thumb Print**
*(When Applicable)*

**Notary Service(s) Performed** ☐ Jurat ☐ Acknowledgment ☐ Oath

Other(Details)

**Date Notarized:** Time:

AM PM

**IDENTIFICATION**

**Document:** Document Date:

☐ Affidavit ☐ Trust ☐ Acknowledgement
☐ Mortgage/Deed ☐ Will ☐ Power of Attorney
☐ Auto Title ☐ Claim ☐ Other: _____

Notary Service Performed at:

Type:

Number:

Issued By:

Expires:

Notes/Comments:

Witness Name/Address: | Witness Signature: | Known Personally: ☐ Yes ☐ No | **RECORD NUMBER 187**

---

**Name of Signer** (printed) | **Signer's Signature** | **Fee Charged:** $

**Signer's FULL Address** | Phone No. | **Right Thumb Print**
*(When Applicable)*

**Notary Service(s) Performed** ☐ Jurat ☐ Acknowledgment ☐ Oath

Other(Details)

**Date Notarized:** Time:

AM PM

**IDENTIFICATION**

**Document:** Document Date:

☐ Affidavit ☐ Trust ☐ Acknowledgement
☐ Mortgage/Deed ☐ Will ☐ Power of Attorney
☐ Auto Title ☐ Claim ☐ Other: _____

Notary Service Performed at:

Type:

Number:

Issued By:

Expires:

Notes/Comments:

Witness Name/Address: | Witness Signature: | Known Personally: ☐ Yes ☐ No | **RECORD NUMBER 188**

---

**Name of Signer** (printed) | **Signer's Signature** | **Fee Charged:** $

**Signer's FULL Address** | Phone No. | **Right Thumb Print**
*(When Applicable)*

**Notary Service(s) Performed** ☐ Jurat ☐ Acknowledgment ☐ Oath

Other(Details)

**Date Notarized:** Time:

AM PM

**IDENTIFICATION**

**Document:** Document Date:

☐ Affidavit ☐ Trust ☐ Acknowledgement
☐ Mortgage/Deed ☐ Will ☐ Power of Attorney
☐ Auto Title ☐ Claim ☐ Other: _____

Notary Service Performed at:

Type:

Number:

Issued By:

Expires:

Notes/Comments:

Witness Name/Address: | Witness Signature: | Known Personally: ☐ Yes ☐ No | **RECORD NUMBER 189**

| Name of Signer (printed) | Signer's Signature | Fee Charged:$ |
| --- | --- | --- |

| Right Thumb Print (When Applicable) | Signer's FULL Address | Phone No. |
| --- | --- | --- |

**Notary Service(s) Performed**  ☐ Jurat  ☐ Acknowledgment  ☐ Oath

Other(Details)

**Date Notarized:**  **Time:**

**AM  PM**

**IDENTIFICATION**

Type:

Number:

Issued By:

Expires:

**Document:**  Document Date:

☐ Affidavit  ☐ Trust  ☐ Acknowledgement
☐ Mortgage/Deed  ☐ Will  ☐ Power of Attorney
☐ Auto Title  ☐ Claim  ☐ Other: _____

Notary Service Performed at:

Notes/Comments:

**RECORD NUMBER 190**

Witness Name/Address:  Witness Signature:

Known Personally:  ☐ Yes  ☐ No

---

| Name of Signer (printed) | Signer's Signature | Fee Charged:$ |
| --- | --- | --- |

| Right Thumb Print (When Applicable) | Signer's FULL Address | Phone No. |
| --- | --- | --- |

**Notary Service(s) Performed**  ☐ Jurat  ☐ Acknowledgment  ☐ Oath

Other(Details)

**Date Notarized:**  **Time:**

**AM  PM**

**IDENTIFICATION**

Type:

Number:

Issued By:

Expires:

**Document:**  Document Date:

☐ Affidavit  ☐ Trust  ☐ Acknowledgement
☐ Mortgage/Deed  ☐ Will  ☐ Power of Attorney
☐ Auto Title  ☐ Claim  ☐ Other: _____

Notary Service Performed at:

Notes/Comments:

**RECORD NUMBER 191**

Witness Name/Address:  Witness Signature:

Known Personally:  ☐ Yes  ☐ No

---

| Name of Signer (printed) | Signer's Signature | Fee Charged:$ |
| --- | --- | --- |

| Right Thumb Print (When Applicable) | Signer's FULL Address | Phone No. |
| --- | --- | --- |

**Notary Service(s) Performed**  ☐ Jurat  ☐ Acknowledgment  ☐ Oath

Other(Details)

**Date Notarized:**  **Time:**

**AM  PM**

**IDENTIFICATION**

Type:

Number:

Issued By:

Expires:

**Document:**  Document Date:

☐ Affidavit  ☐ Trust  ☐ Acknowledgement
☐ Mortgage/Deed  ☐ Will  ☐ Power of Attorney
☐ Auto Title  ☐ Claim  ☐ Other: _____

Notary Service Performed at:

Notes/Comments:

**RECORD NUMBER 192**

Witness Name/Address:  Witness Signature:

Known Personally:  ☐ Yes  ☐ No

| Name of Signer (printed) | Signer's Signature | Fee Charged:$ |
|---|---|---|

Signer's FULL Address                                    Phone No.

Right Thumb Print
*(When Applicable)*

Notary Service(s) Performed   ☐ Jurat   ☐ Acknowledgment   ☐ Oath

Other(Details)

Date Notarized:          Time:

AM  PM

**IDENTIFICATION**

Document:                                    Document Date:

☐ Affidavit      ☐ Trust      ☐ Acknowledgement
☐ Mortgage/Deed  ☐ Will       ☐ Power of Attorney
☐ Auto Title     ☐ Claim      ☐ Other: _____

Notary Service Performed at:

Type:

Number:

Issued By:

Expires:

Notes/Comments:

Witness Name/Address:              Witness Signature:

Known Personally:
☐ Yes  ☐ No

**RECORD NUMBER**
**193**

---

| Name of Signer (printed) | Signer's Signature | Fee Charged:$ |
|---|---|---|

Signer's FULL Address                                    Phone No.

Right Thumb Print
*(When Applicable)*

Notary Service(s) Performed   ☐ Jurat   ☐ Acknowledgment   ☐ Oath

Other(Details)

Date Notarized:          Time:

AM  PM

**IDENTIFICATION**

Document:                                    Document Date:

☐ Affidavit      ☐ Trust      ☐ Acknowledgement
☐ Mortgage/Deed  ☐ Will       ☐ Power of Attorney
☐ Auto Title     ☐ Claim      ☐ Other: _____

Notary Service Performed at:

Type:

Number:

Issued By:

Expires:

Notes/Comments:

Witness Name/Address:              Witness Signature:

Known Personally:
☐ Yes  ☐ No

**RECORD NUMBER**
**194**

---

| Name of Signer (printed) | Signer's Signature | Fee Charged:$ |
|---|---|---|

Signer's FULL Address                                    Phone No.

Right Thumb Print
*(When Applicable)*

Notary Service(s) Performed   ☐ Jurat   ☐ Acknowledgment   ☐ Oath

Other(Details)

Date Notarized:          Time:

AM  PM

**IDENTIFICATION**

Document:                                    Document Date:

☐ Affidavit      ☐ Trust      ☐ Acknowledgement
☐ Mortgage/Deed  ☐ Will       ☐ Power of Attorney
☐ Auto Title     ☐ Claim      ☐ Other: _____

Notary Service Performed at:

Type:

Number:

Issued By:

Expires:

Notes/Comments:

Witness Name/Address:              Witness Signature:

Known Personally:
☐ Yes  ☐ No

**RECORD NUMBER**
**195**

| Name of Signer (printed) | Signer's Signature | Fee Charged:$ |
|---|---|---|

**Right Thumb Print** (When Applicable)

Signer's FULL Address
Phone No.

Notary Service(s) Performed  ☐ Jurat  ☐ Acknowledgment  ☐ Oath

Other(Details)

Date Notarized:  Time:

AM  PM

**IDENTIFICATION**

Notes/Comments:

Document:  Document Date:

☐ Affidavit  ☐ Trust  ☐ Acknowledgement
☐ Mortgage/Deed  ☐ Will  ☐ Power of Attorney
☐ Auto Title  ☐ Claim  ☐ Other: _____

Notary Service Performed at:

Type:

Number:

Issued By:

Expires:

**RECORD NUMBER 196**

Witness Name/Address:  Witness Signature:

Known Personally:

☐ Yes  ☐ No

---

| Name of Signer (printed) | Signer's Signature | Fee Charged:$ |
|---|---|---|

**Right Thumb Print** (When Applicable)

Signer's FULL Address
Phone No.

Notary Service(s) Performed  ☐ Jurat  ☐ Acknowledgment  ☐ Oath

Other(Details)

Date Notarized:  Time:

AM  PM

**IDENTIFICATION**

Notes/Comments:

Document:  Document Date:

☐ Affidavit  ☐ Trust  ☐ Acknowledgement
☐ Mortgage/Deed  ☐ Will  ☐ Power of Attorney
☐ Auto Title  ☐ Claim  ☐ Other: _____

Notary Service Performed at:

Type:

Number:

Issued By:

Expires:

**RECORD NUMBER 197**

Witness Name/Address:  Witness Signature:

Known Personally:

☐ Yes  ☐ No

---

| Name of Signer (printed) | Signer's Signature | Fee Charged:$ |
|---|---|---|

**Right Thumb Print** (When Applicable)

Signer's FULL Address
Phone No.

Notary Service(s) Performed  ☐ Jurat  ☐ Acknowledgment  ☐ Oath

Other(Details)

Date Notarized:  Time:

AM  PM

**IDENTIFICATION**

Notes/Comments:

Document:  Document Date:

☐ Affidavit  ☐ Trust  ☐ Acknowledgement
☐ Mortgage/Deed  ☐ Will  ☐ Power of Attorney
☐ Auto Title  ☐ Claim  ☐ Other: _____

Notary Service Performed at:

Type:

Number:

Issued By:

Expires:

**RECORD NUMBER 198**

Witness Name/Address:  Witness Signature:

Known Personally:

☐ Yes  ☐ No

| Name of Signer (printed) | Signer's Signature | Fee Charged:$ |

Signer's FULL Address                                      Phone No.        Right Thumb Print *(When Applicable)*

Notary Service(s) Performed  ☐ Jurat   ☐ Acknowledgment   ☐ Oath        Date Notarized:      Time:

Other(Details)                                                                      AM  PM

Document:                                    Document Date:      **IDENTIFICATION**        Notes/Comments:
                                                                Type:
☐ Affidavit        ☐ Trust      ☐ Acknowledgement
☐ Mortgage/Deed    ☐ Will       ☐ Power of Attorney          Number:
☐ Auto Title       ☐ Claim      ☐ Other: _____     Issued By:
Notary Service Performed at:                                 Expires:

Witness Name/Address:              Witness Signature:         Known Personally:       **RECORD NUMBER**
                                                             ☐ Yes  ☐ No              **199**

---

| Name of Signer (printed) | Signer's Signature | Fee Charged:$ |

Signer's FULL Address                                      Phone No.        Right Thumb Print *(When Applicable)*

Notary Service(s) Performed  ☐ Jurat   ☐ Acknowledgment   ☐ Oath        Date Notarized:      Time:

Other(Details)                                                                      AM  PM

Document:                                    Document Date:      **IDENTIFICATION**        Notes/Comments:
                                                                Type:
☐ Affidavit        ☐ Trust      ☐ Acknowledgement
☐ Mortgage/Deed    ☐ Will       ☐ Power of Attorney          Number:
☐ Auto Title       ☐ Claim      ☐ Other: _____     Issued By:
Notary Service Performed at:                                 Expires:

Witness Name/Address:              Witness Signature:         Known Personally:       **RECORD NUMBER**
                                                             ☐ Yes  ☐ No              **200**

---

| Name of Signer (printed) | Signer's Signature | Fee Charged:$ |

Signer's FULL Address                                      Phone No.        Right Thumb Print *(When Applicable)*

Notary Service(s) Performed  ☐ Jurat   ☐ Acknowledgment   ☐ Oath        Date Notarized:      Time:

Other(Details)                                                                      AM  PM

Document:                                    Document Date:      **IDENTIFICATION**        Notes/Comments:
                                                                Type:
☐ Affidavit        ☐ Trust      ☐ Acknowledgement
☐ Mortgage/Deed    ☐ Will       ☐ Power of Attorney          Number:
☐ Auto Title       ☐ Claim      ☐ Other: _____     Issued By:
Notary Service Performed at:                                 Expires:

Witness Name/Address:              Witness Signature:         Known Personally:       **RECORD NUMBER**
                                                             ☐ Yes  ☐ No              **201**

| Name of Signer (printed) | Signer's Signature | Fee Charged:$ |
|---|---|---|

| Right Thumb Print (When Applicable) | Signer's FULL Address | Phone No. |
|---|---|---|

Notary Service(s) Performed ☐Jurat ☐Acknowledgment ☐Oath

Other(Details)

**Date Notarized:** Time:

AM PM

**IDENTIFICATION**

Type:

| Notes/Comments: | Document: Document Date: |
|---|---|

☐ Affidavit ☐ Trust ☐ Acknowledgement

☐ Mortgage/Deed ☐ Will ☐ Power of Attorney

☐ Auto Title ☐ Claim ☐ Other: _____

Notary Service Performed at:

Number:

Issued By:

Expires:

**RECORD NUMBER 202**

Witness Name/Address: Witness Signature:

Known Personally:

☐Yes ☐No

---

| Name of Signer (printed) | Signer's Signature | Fee Charged:$ |
|---|---|---|

| Right Thumb Print (When Applicable) | Signer's FULL Address | Phone No. |
|---|---|---|

Notary Service(s) Performed ☐Jurat ☐Acknowledgment ☐Oath

Other(Details)

**Date Notarized:** Time:

AM PM

**IDENTIFICATION**

Type:

| Notes/Comments: | Document: Document Date: |
|---|---|

☐ Affidavit ☐ Trust ☐ Acknowledgement

☐ Mortgage/Deed ☐ Will ☐ Power of Attorney

☐ Auto Title ☐ Claim ☐ Other: _____

Notary Service Performed at:

Number:

Issued By:

Expires:

**RECORD NUMBER 203**

Witness Name/Address: Witness Signature:

Known Personally:

☐Yes ☐No

---

| Name of Signer (printed) | Signer's Signature | Fee Charged:$ |
|---|---|---|

| Right Thumb Print (When Applicable) | Signer's FULL Address | Phone No. |
|---|---|---|

Notary Service(s) Performed ☐Jurat ☐Acknowledgment ☐Oath

Other(Details)

**Date Notarized:** Time:

AM PM

**IDENTIFICATION**

Type:

| Notes/Comments: | Document: Document Date: |
|---|---|

☐ Affidavit ☐ Trust ☐ Acknowledgement

☐ Mortgage/Deed ☐ Will ☐ Power of Attorney

☐ Auto Title ☐ Claim ☐ Other: _____

Notary Service Performed at:

Number:

Issued By:

Expires:

**RECORD NUMBER 204**

Witness Name/Address: Witness Signature:

Known Personally:

☐Yes ☐No

| Name of Signer (printed) | Signer's Signature | Fee Charged:$ |
|---|---|---|

Signer's FULL Address                                      Phone No.

Right Thumb Print
*(When Applicable)*

Notary Service(s) Performed   ☐ Jurat   ☐ Acknowledgment   ☐ Oath

Other(Details)

Date Notarized:        Time:

**AM PM**

Document:                                    Document Date:

**IDENTIFICATION**

Type:

☐ Affidavit      ☐ Trust      ☐ Acknowledgement

☐ Mortgage/Deed  ☐ Will       ☐ Power of Attorney

☐ Auto Title     ☐ Claim      ☐ Other: _____

Number:

Issued By:

Notary Service Performed at:

Expires:

Notes/Comments:

Witness Name/Address:              Witness Signature:

Known Personally:

☐ Yes   ☐ No

**RECORD NUMBER**
**205**

---

| Name of Signer (printed) | Signer's Signature | Fee Charged:$ |
|---|---|---|

Signer's FULL Address                                      Phone No.

Right Thumb Print
*(When Applicable)*

Notary Service(s) Performed   ☐ Jurat   ☐ Acknowledgment   ☐ Oath

Other(Details)

Date Notarized:        Time:

**AM PM**

Document:                                    Document Date:

**IDENTIFICATION**

Type:

☐ Affidavit      ☐ Trust      ☐ Acknowledgement

☐ Mortgage/Deed  ☐ Will       ☐ Power of Attorney

☐ Auto Title     ☐ Claim      ☐ Other: _____

Number:

Issued By:

Notary Service Performed at:

Expires:

Notes/Comments:

Witness Name/Address:              Witness Signature:

Known Personally:

☐ Yes   ☐ No

**RECORD NUMBER**
**206**

---

| Name of Signer (printed) | Signer's Signature | Fee Charged:$ |
|---|---|---|

Signer's FULL Address                                      Phone No.

Right Thumb Print
*(When Applicable)*

Notary Service(s) Performed   ☐ Jurat   ☐ Acknowledgment   ☐ Oath

Other(Details)

Date Notarized:        Time:

**AM PM**

Document:                                    Document Date:

**IDENTIFICATION**

Type:

☐ Affidavit      ☐ Trust      ☐ Acknowledgement

☐ Mortgage/Deed  ☐ Will       ☐ Power of Attorney

☐ Auto Title     ☐ Claim      ☐ Other: _____

Number:

Issued By:

Notary Service Performed at:

Expires:

Notes/Comments:

Witness Name/Address:              Witness Signature:

Known Personally:

☐ Yes   ☐ No

**RECORD NUMBER**
**207**

| Name of Signer *(printed)* | Signer's Signature | Fee Charged:$ |
|---|---|---|

| Right Thumb Print *(When Applicable)* | Signer's FULL Address | Phone No. |
|---|---|---|

| | Notary Service(s) Performed ☐Jurat ☐Acknowledgment ☐Oath  Other(Details) | Date Notarized: Time:  AM PM |
|---|---|---|

| Notes/Comments: | Document: Document Date: | **IDENTIFICATION** |
|---|---|---|
| | ☐ Affidavit ☐ Trust ☐ Acknowledgement | Type: |
| | ☐ Mortgage/Deed ☐ Will ☐ Power of Attorney | Number: |
| | ☐ Auto Title ☐ Claim ☐ Other: _____ | Issued By: |
| | Notary Service Performed at: | Expires: |

| **RECORD NUMBER 208** | Witness Name/Address: Witness Signature: | Known Personally: ☐Yes ☐No |
|---|---|---|

---

| Name of Signer *(printed)* | Signer's Signature | Fee Charged:$ |
|---|---|---|

| Right Thumb Print *(When Applicable)* | Signer's FULL Address | Phone No. |
|---|---|---|

| | Notary Service(s) Performed ☐Jurat ☐Acknowledgment ☐Oath  Other(Details) | Date Notarized: Time:  AM PM |
|---|---|---|

| Notes/Comments: | Document: Document Date: | **IDENTIFICATION** |
|---|---|---|
| | ☐ Affidavit ☐ Trust ☐ Acknowledgement | Type: |
| | ☐ Mortgage/Deed ☐ Will ☐ Power of Attorney | Number: |
| | ☐ Auto Title ☐ Claim ☐ Other: _____ | Issued By: |
| | Notary Service Performed at: | Expires: |

| **RECORD NUMBER 209** | Witness Name/Address: Witness Signature: | Known Personally: ☐Yes ☐No |
|---|---|---|

---

| Name of Signer *(printed)* | Signer's Signature | Fee Charged:$ |
|---|---|---|

| Right Thumb Print *(When Applicable)* | Signer's FULL Address | Phone No. |
|---|---|---|

| | Notary Service(s) Performed ☐Jurat ☐Acknowledgment ☐Oath  Other(Details) | Date Notarized: Time:  AM PM |
|---|---|---|

| Notes/Comments: | Document: Document Date: | **IDENTIFICATION** |
|---|---|---|
| | ☐ Affidavit ☐ Trust ☐ Acknowledgement | Type: |
| | ☐ Mortgage/Deed ☐ Will ☐ Power of Attorney | Number: |
| | ☐ Auto Title ☐ Claim ☐ Other: _____ | Issued By: |
| | Notary Service Performed at: | Expires: |

| **RECORD NUMBER 210** | Witness Name/Address: Witness Signature: | Known Personally: ☐Yes ☐No |
|---|---|---|

Name of Signer *(printed)* | Signer's Signature | Fee Charged:$

Signer's FULL Address | Phone No. | Right Thumb Print *(When Applicable)*

Notary Service(s) Performed ☐ Jurat ☐ Acknowledgment ☐ Oath

Other(Details)

Date Notarized: Time:

AM PM

Document: Document Date:

**IDENTIFICATION**

Type:

☐ Affidavit ☐ Trust ☐ Acknowledgement
☐ Mortgage/Deed ☐ Will ☐ Power of Attorney
☐ Auto Title ☐ Claim ☐ Other: _____

Number:

Issued By:

Notary Service Performed at:

Expires:

Notes/Comments:

Witness Name/Address: | Witness Signature: | Known Personally: ☐ Yes ☐ No

**RECORD NUMBER 211**

---

Name of Signer *(printed)* | Signer's Signature | Fee Charged:$

Signer's FULL Address | Phone No. | Right Thumb Print *(When Applicable)*

Notary Service(s) Performed ☐ Jurat ☐ Acknowledgment ☐ Oath

Other(Details)

Date Notarized: Time:

AM PM

Document: Document Date:

**IDENTIFICATION**

Type:

☐ Affidavit ☐ Trust ☐ Acknowledgement
☐ Mortgage/Deed ☐ Will ☐ Power of Attorney
☐ Auto Title ☐ Claim ☐ Other: _____

Number:

Issued By:

Notary Service Performed at:

Expires:

Notes/Comments:

Witness Name/Address: | Witness Signature: | Known Personally: ☐ Yes ☐ No

**RECORD NUMBER 212**

---

Name of Signer *(printed)* | Signer's Signature | Fee Charged:$

Signer's FULL Address | Phone No. | Right Thumb Print *(When Applicable)*

Notary Service(s) Performed ☐ Jurat ☐ Acknowledgment ☐ Oath

Other(Details)

Date Notarized: Time:

AM PM

Document: Document Date:

**IDENTIFICATION**

Type:

☐ Affidavit ☐ Trust ☐ Acknowledgement
☐ Mortgage/Deed ☐ Will ☐ Power of Attorney
☐ Auto Title ☐ Claim ☐ Other: _____

Number:

Issued By:

Notary Service Performed at:

Expires:

Notes/Comments:

Witness Name/Address: | Witness Signature: | Known Personally: ☐ Yes ☐ No

**RECORD NUMBER 213**

**Name of Signer** (*printed*) | **Signer's Signature** | **Fee Charged:** $

**Right Thumb Print** (*When Applicable*)

**Signer's FULL Address** | **Phone No.**

**Notary Service(s) Performed** ☐Jurat ☐Acknowledgment ☐Oath

Other(Details)

**Date Notarized:** | **Time:**

AM PM

**Notes/Comments:**

**Document:** | **Document Date:**

☐ Affidavit ☐ Trust ☐ Acknowledgement
☐ Mortgage/Deed ☐ Will ☐ Power of Attorney
☐ Auto Title ☐ Claim ☐ Other: _____

Notary Service Performed at:

**IDENTIFICATION**
Type:
Number:
Issued By:
Expires:

**RECORD NUMBER 214**

Witness Name/Address: | Witness Signature:

**Known Personally:**
☐Yes ☐No

---

**Name of Signer** (*printed*) | **Signer's Signature** | **Fee Charged:** $

**Right Thumb Print** (*When Applicable*)

**Signer's FULL Address** | **Phone No.**

**Notary Service(s) Performed** ☐Jurat ☐Acknowledgment ☐Oath

Other(Details)

**Date Notarized:** | **Time:**

AM PM

**Notes/Comments:**

**Document:** | **Document Date:**

☐ Affidavit ☐ Trust ☐ Acknowledgement
☐ Mortgage/Deed ☐ Will ☐ Power of Attorney
☐ Auto Title ☐ Claim ☐ Other: _____

Notary Service Performed at:

**IDENTIFICATION**
Type:
Number:
Issued By:
Expires:

**RECORD NUMBER 215**

Witness Name/Address: | Witness Signature:

**Known Personally:**
☐Yes ☐No

---

**Name of Signer** (*printed*) | **Signer's Signature** | **Fee Charged:** $

**Right Thumb Print** (*When Applicable*)

**Signer's FULL Address** | **Phone No.**

**Notary Service(s) Performed** ☐Jurat ☐Acknowledgment ☐Oath

Other(Details)

**Date Notarized:** | **Time:**

AM PM

**Notes/Comments:**

**Document:** | **Document Date:**

☐ Affidavit ☐ Trust ☐ Acknowledgement
☐ Mortgage/Deed ☐ Will ☐ Power of Attorney
☐ Auto Title ☐ Claim ☐ Other: _____

Notary Service Performed at:

**IDENTIFICATION**
Type:
Number:
Issued By:
Expires:

**RECORD NUMBER 216**

Witness Name/Address: | Witness Signature:

**Known Personally:**
☐Yes ☐No

| Name of Signer (printed) | Signer's Signature | Fee Charged: $ |
|---|---|---|

Signer's FULL Address                                       Phone No.

Right Thumb Print
(When Applicable)

Notary Service(s) Performed   ☐ Jurat   ☐ Acknowledgment   ☐ Oath

Date Notarized:        Time:

Other(Details)

AM  PM

**IDENTIFICATION**

Document:                                    Document Date:

Type:

☐ Affidavit        ☐ Trust        ☐ Acknowledgement

Number:

☐ Mortgage/Deed    ☐ Will         ☐ Power of Attorney

Issued By:

☐ Auto Title       ☐ Claim        ☐ Other: _____

Notary Service Performed at:

Expires:

Notes/Comments:

Witness Name/Address:               Witness Signature:

Known Personally:

☐ Yes   ☐ No

**RECORD NUMBER
217**

---

| Name of Signer (printed) | Signer's Signature | Fee Charged: $ |
|---|---|---|

Signer's FULL Address                                       Phone No.

Right Thumb Print
(When Applicable)

Notary Service(s) Performed   ☐ Jurat   ☐ Acknowledgment   ☐ Oath

Date Notarized:        Time:

Other(Details)

AM  PM

**IDENTIFICATION**

Document:                                    Document Date:

Type:

☐ Affidavit        ☐ Trust        ☐ Acknowledgement

Number:

☐ Mortgage/Deed    ☐ Will         ☐ Power of Attorney

Issued By:

☐ Auto Title       ☐ Claim        ☐ Other: _____

Notary Service Performed at:

Expires:

Notes/Comments:

Witness Name/Address:               Witness Signature:

Known Personally:

☐ Yes   ☐ No

**RECORD NUMBER
218**

---

| Name of Signer (printed) | Signer's Signature | Fee Charged: $ |
|---|---|---|

Signer's FULL Address                                       Phone No.

Right Thumb Print
(When Applicable)

Notary Service(s) Performed   ☐ Jurat   ☐ Acknowledgment   ☐ Oath

Date Notarized:        Time:

Other(Details)

AM  PM

**IDENTIFICATION**

Document:                                    Document Date:

Type:

☐ Affidavit        ☐ Trust        ☐ Acknowledgement

Number:

☐ Mortgage/Deed    ☐ Will         ☐ Power of Attorney

Issued By:

☐ Auto Title       ☐ Claim        ☐ Other: _____

Notary Service Performed at:

Expires:

Notes/Comments:

Witness Name/Address:               Witness Signature:

Known Personally:

☐ Yes   ☐ No

**RECORD NUMBER
219**

| Name of Signer *(printed)* | Signer's Signature | Fee Charged:$ |
|---|---|---|

| Right Thumb Print *(When Applicable)* | Signer's FULL Address | Phone No. |
|---|---|---|

Notary Service(s) Performed ☐ Jurat ☐ Acknowledgment ☐ Oath

Other(Details)

| | Document: | Document Date: | **IDENTIFICATION** |
|---|---|---|---|

Notes/Comments:

☐ Affidavit ☐ Trust ☐ Acknowledgement
☐ Mortgage/Deed ☐ Will ☐ Power of Attorney
☐ Auto Title ☐ Claim ☐ Other: _____

Notary Service Performed at:

Type:

Number:

Issued By:

Expires:

| **RECORD NUMBER** **220** | Witness Name/Address: | Witness Signature: | Known Personally: ☐Yes ☐No |
|---|---|---|---|

---

| Name of Signer *(printed)* | Signer's Signature | Fee Charged:$ |
|---|---|---|

| Right Thumb Print *(When Applicable)* | Signer's FULL Address | Phone No. |
|---|---|---|

Notary Service(s) Performed ☐ Jurat ☐ Acknowledgment ☐ Oath

Other(Details)

| | Document: | Document Date: | **IDENTIFICATION** |
|---|---|---|---|

Notes/Comments:

☐ Affidavit ☐ Trust ☐ Acknowledgement
☐ Mortgage/Deed ☐ Will ☐ Power of Attorney
☐ Auto Title ☐ Claim ☐ Other: _____

Notary Service Performed at:

Type:

Number:

Issued By:

Expires:

| **RECORD NUMBER** **221** | Witness Name/Address: | Witness Signature: | Known Personally: ☐Yes ☐No |
|---|---|---|---|

---

| Name of Signer *(printed)* | Signer's Signature | Fee Charged:$ |
|---|---|---|

| Right Thumb Print *(When Applicable)* | Signer's FULL Address | Phone No. |
|---|---|---|

Notary Service(s) Performed ☐ Jurat ☐ Acknowledgment ☐ Oath

Other(Details)

| | Document: | Document Date: | **IDENTIFICATION** |
|---|---|---|---|

Notes/Comments:

☐ Affidavit ☐ Trust ☐ Acknowledgement
☐ Mortgage/Deed ☐ Will ☐ Power of Attorney
☐ Auto Title ☐ Claim ☐ Other: _____

Notary Service Performed at:

Type:

Number:

Issued By:

Expires:

| **RECORD NUMBER** **222** | Witness Name/Address: | Witness Signature: | Known Personally: ☐Yes ☐No |
|---|---|---|---|

| Name of Signer (printed) | Signer's Signature | Fee Charged:$ |
|---|---|---|

Signer's FULL Address                                    Phone No.

Right Thumb Print *(When Applicable)*

Notary Service(s) Performed   ☐ Jurat   ☐ Acknowledgment   ☐ Oath

Other(Details)

Date Notarized:      Time:

**AM  PM**

Document:                                    Document Date:

**IDENTIFICATION**

Type:

☐ Affidavit       ☐ Trust       ☐ Acknowledgement

☐ Mortgage/Deed   ☐ Will        ☐ Power of Attorney

☐ Auto Title      ☐ Claim       ☐ Other: _____

Notary Service Performed at:

Number:

Issued By:

Expires:

Notes/Comments:

Witness Name/Address:                Witness Signature:

Known Personally:

☐ Yes  ☐ No

**RECORD NUMBER
223**

---

| Name of Signer (printed) | Signer's Signature | Fee Charged:$ |
|---|---|---|

Signer's FULL Address                                    Phone No.

Right Thumb Print *(When Applicable)*

Notary Service(s) Performed   ☐ Jurat   ☐ Acknowledgment   ☐ Oath

Other(Details)

Date Notarized:      Time:

**AM  PM**

Document:                                    Document Date:

**IDENTIFICATION**

Type:

☐ Affidavit       ☐ Trust       ☐ Acknowledgement

☐ Mortgage/Deed   ☐ Will        ☐ Power of Attorney

☐ Auto Title      ☐ Claim       ☐ Other: _____

Notary Service Performed at:

Number:

Issued By:

Expires:

Notes/Comments:

Witness Name/Address:                Witness Signature:

Known Personally:

☐ Yes  ☐ No

**RECORD NUMBER
224**

---

| Name of Signer (printed) | Signer's Signature | Fee Charged:$ |
|---|---|---|

Signer's FULL Address                                    Phone No.

Right Thumb Print *(When Applicable)*

Notary Service(s) Performed   ☐ Jurat   ☐ Acknowledgment   ☐ Oath

Other(Details)

Date Notarized:      Time:

**AM  PM**

Document:                                    Document Date:

**IDENTIFICATION**

Type:

☐ Affidavit       ☐ Trust       ☐ Acknowledgement

☐ Mortgage/Deed   ☐ Will        ☐ Power of Attorney

☐ Auto Title      ☐ Claim       ☐ Other: _____

Notary Service Performed at:

Number:

Issued By:

Expires:

Notes/Comments:

Witness Name/Address:                Witness Signature:

Known Personally:

☐ Yes  ☐ No

**RECORD NUMBER
225**

| Name of Signer (printed) | Signer's Signature | Fee Charged:$ |
|---|---|---|

| Right Thumb Print (When Applicable) | Signer's FULL Address | Phone No. |

**Notary Service(s) Performed** ☐Jurat ☐Acknowledgment ☐Oath

Other(Details)

| Date Notarized: | Time: |
|---|---|
| | AM PM |

**Notes/Comments:**

Document:            Document Date:

☐ Affidavit     ☐ Trust     ☐ Acknowledgement
☐ Mortgage/Deed     ☐ Will     ☐ Power of Attorney
☐ Auto Title     ☐ Claim     ☐ Other: _____

Notary Service Performed at:

**IDENTIFICATION**
Type:
Number:
Issued By:
Expires:

**RECORD NUMBER 226**

Witness Name/Address:         Witness Signature:

Known Personally:
☐Yes ☐No

---

| Name of Signer (printed) | Signer's Signature | Fee Charged:$ |
|---|---|---|

| Right Thumb Print (When Applicable) | Signer's FULL Address | Phone No. |

**Notary Service(s) Performed** ☐Jurat ☐Acknowledgment ☐Oath

Other(Details)

| Date Notarized: | Time: |
|---|---|
| | AM PM |

**Notes/Comments:**

Document:            Document Date:

☐ Affidavit     ☐ Trust     ☐ Acknowledgement
☐ Mortgage/Deed     ☐ Will     ☐ Power of Attorney
☐ Auto Title     ☐ Claim     ☐ Other: _____

Notary Service Performed at:

**IDENTIFICATION**
Type:
Number:
Issued By:
Expires:

**RECORD NUMBER 227**

Witness Name/Address:         Witness Signature:

Known Personally:
☐Yes ☐No

---

| Name of Signer (printed) | Signer's Signature | Fee Charged:$ |
|---|---|---|

| Right Thumb Print (When Applicable) | Signer's FULL Address | Phone No. |

**Notary Service(s) Performed** ☐Jurat ☐Acknowledgment ☐Oath

Other(Details)

| Date Notarized: | Time: |
|---|---|
| | AM PM |

**Notes/Comments:**

Document:            Document Date:

☐ Affidavit     ☐ Trust     ☐ Acknowledgement
☐ Mortgage/Deed     ☐ Will     ☐ Power of Attorney
☐ Auto Title     ☐ Claim     ☐ Other: _____

Notary Service Performed at:

**IDENTIFICATION**
Type:
Number:
Issued By:
Expires:

**RECORD NUMBER 228**

Witness Name/Address:         Witness Signature:

Known Personally:
☐Yes ☐No

## Record Number 229

**Name of Signer** *(printed)*

**Signer's Signature**

**Fee Charged:** $

**Signer's FULL Address**

**Phone No.**

**Right Thumb Print** *(When Applicable)*

**Notary Service(s) Performed** ☐ Jurat ☐ Acknowledgment ☐ Oath

**Date Notarized:** **Time:**

AM PM

**Other(Details)**

**Document:** **Document Date:**

**IDENTIFICATION**

**Type:**

☐ Affidavit ☐ Trust ☐ Acknowledgement

**Number:**

☐ Mortgage/Deed ☐ Will ☐ Power of Attorney

☐ Auto Title ☐ Claim ☐ Other: _____

**Issued By:**

**Notary Service Performed at:**

**Expires:**

**Witness Name/Address:** **Witness Signature:**

**Known Personally:**

☐ Yes ☐ No

**Notes/Comments:**

**RECORD NUMBER 229**

---

## Record Number 230

**Name of Signer** *(printed)*

**Signer's Signature**

**Fee Charged:** $

**Signer's FULL Address**

**Phone No.**

**Right Thumb Print** *(When Applicable)*

**Notary Service(s) Performed** ☐ Jurat ☐ Acknowledgment ☐ Oath

**Date Notarized:** **Time:**

AM PM

**Other(Details)**

**Document:** **Document Date:**

**IDENTIFICATION**

**Type:**

☐ Affidavit ☐ Trust ☐ Acknowledgement

**Number:**

☐ Mortgage/Deed ☐ Will ☐ Power of Attorney

☐ Auto Title ☐ Claim ☐ Other: _____

**Issued By:**

**Notary Service Performed at:**

**Expires:**

**Witness Name/Address:** **Witness Signature:**

**Known Personally:**

☐ Yes ☐ No

**Notes/Comments:**

**RECORD NUMBER 230**

---

## Record Number 231

**Name of Signer** *(printed)*

**Signer's Signature**

**Fee Charged:** $

**Signer's FULL Address**

**Phone No.**

**Right Thumb Print** *(When Applicable)*

**Notary Service(s) Performed** ☐ Jurat ☐ Acknowledgment ☐ Oath

**Date Notarized:** **Time:**

AM PM

**Other(Details)**

**Document:** **Document Date:**

**IDENTIFICATION**

**Type:**

☐ Affidavit ☐ Trust ☐ Acknowledgement

**Number:**

☐ Mortgage/Deed ☐ Will ☐ Power of Attorney

☐ Auto Title ☐ Claim ☐ Other: _____

**Issued By:**

**Notary Service Performed at:**

**Expires:**

**Witness Name/Address:** **Witness Signature:**

**Known Personally:**

☐ Yes ☐ No

**Notes/Comments:**

**RECORD NUMBER 231**

| Name of Signer *(printed)* | Signer's Signature | Fee Charged:$ |
| --- | --- | --- |

| Right Thumb Print *(When Applicable)* | Signer's FULL Address | Phone No. |
| --- | --- | --- |

Notary Service(s) Performed ☐Jurat ☐Acknowledgment ☐Oath

Other(Details)

| Date Notarized: | Time: |
| --- | --- |

**AM PM**

**IDENTIFICATION**

Type:

| Notes/Comments: | Document: | Document Date: |
| --- | --- | --- |

☐ Affidavit ☐ Trust ☐ Acknowledgement

☐ Mortgage/Deed ☐ Will ☐ Power of Attorney

☐ Auto Title ☐ Claim ☐ Other: _____

Notary Service Performed at:

Number:

Issued By:

Expires:

| **RECORD NUMBER 232** | Witness Name/Address: | Witness Signature: | Known Personally: |
| --- | --- | --- | --- |

☐**Yes** ☐**No**

---

| Name of Signer *(printed)* | Signer's Signature | Fee Charged:$ |
| --- | --- | --- |

| Right Thumb Print *(When Applicable)* | Signer's FULL Address | Phone No. |
| --- | --- | --- |

Notary Service(s) Performed ☐Jurat ☐Acknowledgment ☐Oath

Other(Details)

| Date Notarized: | Time: |
| --- | --- |

**AM PM**

**IDENTIFICATION**

Type:

| Notes/Comments: | Document: | Document Date: |
| --- | --- | --- |

☐ Affidavit ☐ Trust ☐ Acknowledgement

☐ Mortgage/Deed ☐ Will ☐ Power of Attorney

☐ Auto Title ☐ Claim ☐ Other: _____

Notary Service Performed at:

Number:

Issued By:

Expires:

| **RECORD NUMBER 233** | Witness Name/Address: | Witness Signature: | Known Personally: |
| --- | --- | --- | --- |

☐**Yes** ☐**No**

---

| Name of Signer *(printed)* | Signer's Signature | Fee Charged:$ |
| --- | --- | --- |

| Right Thumb Print *(When Applicable)* | Signer's FULL Address | Phone No. |
| --- | --- | --- |

Notary Service(s) Performed ☐Jurat ☐Acknowledgment ☐Oath

Other(Details)

| Date Notarized: | Time: |
| --- | --- |

**AM PM**

**IDENTIFICATION**

Type:

| Notes/Comments: | Document: | Document Date: |
| --- | --- | --- |

☐ Affidavit ☐ Trust ☐ Acknowledgement

☐ Mortgage/Deed ☐ Will ☐ Power of Attorney

☐ Auto Title ☐ Claim ☐ Other: _____

Notary Service Performed at:

Number:

Issued By:

Expires:

| **RECORD NUMBER 234** | Witness Name/Address: | Witness Signature: | Known Personally: |
| --- | --- | --- | --- |

☐**Yes** ☐**No**

| Name of Signer *(printed)* | Signer's Signature | Fee Charged:$ |
|---|---|---|

Signer's FULL Address — Phone No. — Right Thumb Print *(When Applicable)*

Notary Service(s) Performed ☐ Jurat ☐ Acknowledgment ☐ Oath — Date Notarized: — Time:

Other(Details) — AM PM

Document: — Document Date: — **IDENTIFICATION**
Type:

☐ Affidavit ☐ Trust ☐ Acknowledgement — Number:
☐ Mortgage/Deed ☐ Will ☐ Power of Attorney — Issued By:
☐ Auto Title ☐ Claim ☐ Other: _____ — Expires:

Notary Service Performed at:

Witness Name/Address: — Witness Signature: — Known Personally: ☐ Yes ☐ No — Notes/Comments:

**RECORD NUMBER 235**

---

| Name of Signer *(printed)* | Signer's Signature | Fee Charged:$ |
|---|---|---|

Signer's FULL Address — Phone No. — Right Thumb Print *(When Applicable)*

Notary Service(s) Performed ☐ Jurat ☐ Acknowledgment ☐ Oath — Date Notarized: — Time:

Other(Details) — AM PM

Document: — Document Date: — **IDENTIFICATION**
Type:

☐ Affidavit ☐ Trust ☐ Acknowledgement — Number:
☐ Mortgage/Deed ☐ Will ☐ Power of Attorney — Issued By:
☐ Auto Title ☐ Claim ☐ Other: _____ — Expires:

Notary Service Performed at:

Witness Name/Address: — Witness Signature: — Known Personally: ☐ Yes ☐ No — Notes/Comments:

**RECORD NUMBER 236**

---

| Name of Signer *(printed)* | Signer's Signature | Fee Charged:$ |
|---|---|---|

Signer's FULL Address — Phone No. — Right Thumb Print *(When Applicable)*

Notary Service(s) Performed ☐ Jurat ☐ Acknowledgment ☐ Oath — Date Notarized: — Time:

Other(Details) — AM PM

Document: — Document Date: — **IDENTIFICATION**
Type:

☐ Affidavit ☐ Trust ☐ Acknowledgement — Number:
☐ Mortgage/Deed ☐ Will ☐ Power of Attorney — Issued By:
☐ Auto Title ☐ Claim ☐ Other: _____ — Expires:

Notary Service Performed at:

Witness Name/Address: — Witness Signature: — Known Personally: ☐ Yes ☐ No — Notes/Comments:

**RECORD NUMBER 237**

| Name of Signer *(printed)* | Signer's Signature | Fee Charged:$ |
| --- | --- | --- |

| Right Thumb Print *(When Applicable)* | Signer's FULL Address | Phone No. |
| --- | --- | --- |
| | Notary Service(s) Performed ☐Jurat ☐Acknowledgment ☐Oath<br>Other(Details) | Date Notarized: Time:<br><br>AM PM |

**Notes/Comments:**

Document: Document Date:

- ☐ Affidavit
- ☐ Mortgage/Deed
- ☐ Auto Title
- ☐ Trust
- ☐ Will
- ☐ Claim
- ☐ Acknowledgement
- ☐ Power of Attorney
- ☐ Other: _____

Notary Service Performed at:

**IDENTIFICATION**
Type:
Number:
Issued By:
Expires:

**RECORD NUMBER 238**

Witness Name/Address: Witness Signature:

Known Personally:
☐Yes ☐No

---

| Name of Signer *(printed)* | Signer's Signature | Fee Charged:$ |
| --- | --- | --- |

| Right Thumb Print *(When Applicable)* | Signer's FULL Address | Phone No. |
| --- | --- | --- |
| | Notary Service(s) Performed ☐Jurat ☐Acknowledgment ☐Oath<br>Other(Details) | Date Notarized: Time:<br><br>AM PM |

**Notes/Comments:**

Document: Document Date:

- ☐ Affidavit
- ☐ Mortgage/Deed
- ☐ Auto Title
- ☐ Trust
- ☐ Will
- ☐ Claim
- ☐ Acknowledgement
- ☐ Power of Attorney
- ☐ Other: _____

Notary Service Performed at:

**IDENTIFICATION**
Type:
Number:
Issued By:
Expires:

**RECORD NUMBER 239**

Witness Name/Address: Witness Signature:

Known Personally:
☐Yes ☐No

---

| Name of Signer *(printed)* | Signer's Signature | Fee Charged:$ |
| --- | --- | --- |

| Right Thumb Print *(When Applicable)* | Signer's FULL Address | Phone No. |
| --- | --- | --- |
| | Notary Service(s) Performed ☐Jurat ☐Acknowledgment ☐Oath<br>Other(Details) | Date Notarized: Time:<br><br>AM PM |

**Notes/Comments:**

Document: Document Date:

- ☐ Affidavit
- ☐ Mortgage/Deed
- ☐ Auto Title
- ☐ Trust
- ☐ Will
- ☐ Claim
- ☐ Acknowledgement
- ☐ Power of Attorney
- ☐ Other: _____

Notary Service Performed at:

**IDENTIFICATION**
Type:
Number:
Issued By:
Expires:

**RECORD NUMBER 240**

Witness Name/Address: Witness Signature:

Known Personally:
☐Yes ☐No

| Name of Signer (printed) | Signer's Signature | Fee Charged:$ |
|---|---|---|

Signer's FULL Address          Phone No.          Right Thumb Print (When Applicable)

Notary Service(s) Performed  ☐ Jurat  ☐ Acknowledgment  ☐ Oath

Other(Details)

Date Notarized:          Time:

AM  PM

**Document:**          Document Date:

☐ Affidavit      ☐ Trust    ☐ Acknowledgement
☐ Mortgage/Deed  ☐ Will     ☐ Power of Attorney
☐ Auto Title     ☐ Claim    ☐ Other: _____

Notary Service Performed at:

**IDENTIFICATION**

Type:

Number:

Issued By:

Expires:

Notes/Comments:

Witness Name/Address:          Witness Signature:

Known Personally:   ☐ Yes  ☐ No

**RECORD NUMBER 241**

---

| Name of Signer (printed) | Signer's Signature | Fee Charged:$ |
|---|---|---|

Signer's FULL Address          Phone No.          Right Thumb Print (When Applicable)

Notary Service(s) Performed  ☐ Jurat  ☐ Acknowledgment  ☐ Oath

Other(Details)

Date Notarized:          Time:

AM  PM

**Document:**          Document Date:

☐ Affidavit      ☐ Trust    ☐ Acknowledgement
☐ Mortgage/Deed  ☐ Will     ☐ Power of Attorney
☐ Auto Title     ☐ Claim    ☐ Other: _____

Notary Service Performed at:

**IDENTIFICATION**

Type:

Number:

Issued By:

Expires:

Notes/Comments:

Witness Name/Address:          Witness Signature:

Known Personally:   ☐ Yes  ☐ No

**RECORD NUMBER 242**

---

| Name of Signer (printed) | Signer's Signature | Fee Charged:$ |
|---|---|---|

Signer's FULL Address          Phone No.          Right Thumb Print (When Applicable)

Notary Service(s) Performed  ☐ Jurat  ☐ Acknowledgment  ☐ Oath

Other(Details)

Date Notarized:          Time:

AM  PM

**Document:**          Document Date:

☐ Affidavit      ☐ Trust    ☐ Acknowledgement
☐ Mortgage/Deed  ☐ Will     ☐ Power of Attorney
☐ Auto Title     ☐ Claim    ☐ Other: _____

Notary Service Performed at:

**IDENTIFICATION**

Type:

Number:

Issued By:

Expires:

Notes/Comments:

Witness Name/Address:          Witness Signature:

Known Personally:   ☐ Yes  ☐ No

**RECORD NUMBER 243**

| Name of Signer (printed) | Signer's Signature | Fee Charged: $ |
|---|---|---|

| Right Thumb Print (When Applicable) | Signer's FULL Address | Phone No. |
|---|---|---|
| | Notary Service(s) Performed ☐Jurat ☐Acknowledgment ☐Oath<br>Other(Details) | Date Notarized: Time:<br><br>AM PM |
| Notes/Comments: | Document: Document Date:<br>☐ Affidavit ☐ Trust ☐ Acknowledgement<br>☐ Mortgage/Deed ☐ Will ☐ Power of Attorney<br>☐ Auto Title ☐ Claim ☐ Other: _____<br>Notary Service Performed at: | **IDENTIFICATION**<br>Type:<br>Number:<br>Issued By:<br>Expires: |
| **RECORD NUMBER 244** | Witness Name/Address: Witness Signature: | Known Personally:<br>☐Yes ☐No |

| Name of Signer (printed) | Signer's Signature | Fee Charged: $ |
|---|---|---|

| Right Thumb Print (When Applicable) | Signer's FULL Address | Phone No. |
|---|---|---|
| | Notary Service(s) Performed ☐Jurat ☐Acknowledgment ☐Oath<br>Other(Details) | Date Notarized: Time:<br><br>AM PM |
| Notes/Comments: | Document: Document Date:<br>☐ Affidavit ☐ Trust ☐ Acknowledgement<br>☐ Mortgage/Deed ☐ Will ☐ Power of Attorney<br>☐ Auto Title ☐ Claim ☐ Other: _____<br>Notary Service Performed at: | **IDENTIFICATION**<br>Type:<br>Number:<br>Issued By:<br>Expires: |
| **RECORD NUMBER 245** | Witness Name/Address: Witness Signature: | Known Personally:<br>☐Yes ☐No |

| Name of Signer (printed) | Signer's Signature | Fee Charged: $ |
|---|---|---|

| Right Thumb Print (When Applicable) | Signer's FULL Address | Phone No. |
|---|---|---|
| | Notary Service(s) Performed ☐Jurat ☐Acknowledgment ☐Oath<br>Other(Details) | Date Notarized: Time:<br><br>AM PM |
| Notes/Comments: | Document: Document Date:<br>☐ Affidavit ☐ Trust ☐ Acknowledgement<br>☐ Mortgage/Deed ☐ Will ☐ Power of Attorney<br>☐ Auto Title ☐ Claim ☐ Other: _____<br>Notary Service Performed at: | **IDENTIFICATION**<br>Type:<br>Number:<br>Issued By:<br>Expires: |
| **RECORD NUMBER 246** | Witness Name/Address: Witness Signature: | Known Personally:<br>☐Yes ☐No |

## Record Number 247

Name of Signer (printed)

Signer's Signature

Fee Charged: $

Signer's FULL Address

Phone No.

Right Thumb Print
(When Applicable)

Notary Service(s) Performed   ☐ Jurat   ☐ Acknowledgment   ☐ Oath

Other(Details)

Date Notarized:   Time:

AM   PM

Document:   Document Date:

**IDENTIFICATION**

Type:

Notes/Comments:

☐ Affidavit   ☐ Trust   ☐ Acknowledgement

☐ Mortgage/Deed   ☐ Will   ☐ Power of Attorney

☐ Auto Title   ☐ Claim   ☐ Other: _____

Number:

Issued By:

Notary Service Performed at:

Expires:

Witness Name/Address:

Witness Signature:

Known Personally:

☐ Yes   ☐ No

**RECORD NUMBER 247**

---

## Record Number 248

Name of Signer (printed)

Signer's Signature

Fee Charged: $

Signer's FULL Address

Phone No.

Right Thumb Print
(When Applicable)

Notary Service(s) Performed   ☐ Jurat   ☐ Acknowledgment   ☐ Oath

Other(Details)

Date Notarized:   Time:

AM   PM

Document:   Document Date:

**IDENTIFICATION**

Type:

Notes/Comments:

☐ Affidavit   ☐ Trust   ☐ Acknowledgement

☐ Mortgage/Deed   ☐ Will   ☐ Power of Attorney

☐ Auto Title   ☐ Claim   ☐ Other: _____

Number:

Issued By:

Notary Service Performed at:

Expires:

Witness Name/Address:

Witness Signature:

Known Personally:

☐ Yes   ☐ No

**RECORD NUMBER 248**

---

## Record Number 249

Name of Signer (printed)

Signer's Signature

Fee Charged: $

Signer's FULL Address

Phone No.

Right Thumb Print
(When Applicable)

Notary Service(s) Performed   ☐ Jurat   ☐ Acknowledgment   ☐ Oath

Other(Details)

Date Notarized:   Time:

AM   PM

Document:   Document Date:

**IDENTIFICATION**

Type:

Notes/Comments:

☐ Affidavit   ☐ Trust   ☐ Acknowledgement

☐ Mortgage/Deed   ☐ Will   ☐ Power of Attorney

☐ Auto Title   ☐ Claim   ☐ Other: _____

Number:

Issued By:

Notary Service Performed at:

Expires:

Witness Name/Address:

Witness Signature:

Known Personally:

☐ Yes   ☐ No

**RECORD NUMBER 249**

| Name of Signer *(printed)* | Signer's Signature | Fee Charged:$ |
|---|---|---|

| Right Thumb Print *(When Applicable)* | Signer's FULL Address | Phone No. |
|---|---|---|
| | Notary Service(s) Performed ☐Jurat ☐Acknowledgment ☐Oath<br>Other(Details) | Date Notarized: Time:<br><br>AM PM |
| Notes/Comments: | Document: Document Date:<br>☐ Affidavit ☐ Trust ☐ Acknowledgement<br>☐ Mortgage/Deed ☐ Will ☐ Power of Attorney<br>☐ Auto Title ☐ Claim ☐ Other: _____<br>Notary Service Performed at: | **IDENTIFICATION**<br>Type:<br>Number:<br>Issued By:<br>Expires: |
| **RECORD NUMBER 250** | Witness Name/Address: Witness Signature: | Known Personally:<br>☐Yes ☐No |

| Name of Signer *(printed)* | Signer's Signature | Fee Charged:$ |
|---|---|---|

| Right Thumb Print *(When Applicable)* | Signer's FULL Address | Phone No. |
|---|---|---|
| | Notary Service(s) Performed ☐Jurat ☐Acknowledgment ☐Oath<br>Other(Details) | Date Notarized: Time:<br><br>AM PM |
| Notes/Comments: | Document: Document Date:<br>☐ Affidavit ☐ Trust ☐ Acknowledgement<br>☐ Mortgage/Deed ☐ Will ☐ Power of Attorney<br>☐ Auto Title ☐ Claim ☐ Other: _____<br>Notary Service Performed at: | **IDENTIFICATION**<br>Type:<br>Number:<br>Issued By:<br>Expires: |
| **RECORD NUMBER 251** | Witness Name/Address: Witness Signature: | Known Personally:<br>☐Yes ☐No |

| Name of Signer *(printed)* | Signer's Signature | Fee Charged:$ |
|---|---|---|

| Right Thumb Print *(When Applicable)* | Signer's FULL Address | Phone No. |
|---|---|---|
| | Notary Service(s) Performed ☐Jurat ☐Acknowledgment ☐Oath<br>Other(Details) | Date Notarized: Time:<br><br>AM PM |
| Notes/Comments: | Document: Document Date:<br>☐ Affidavit ☐ Trust ☐ Acknowledgement<br>☐ Mortgage/Deed ☐ Will ☐ Power of Attorney<br>☐ Auto Title ☐ Claim ☐ Other: _____<br>Notary Service Performed at: | **IDENTIFICATION**<br>Type:<br>Number:<br>Issued By:<br>Expires: |
| **RECORD NUMBER 252** | Witness Name/Address: Witness Signature: | Known Personally:<br>☐Yes ☐No |

| Name of Signer *(printed)* | Signer's Signature | Fee Charged:$ |
|---|---|---|

Signer's FULL Address      Phone No.

Right Thumb Print
*(When Applicable)*

Notary Service(s) Performed   ☐ Jurat   ☐ Acknowledgment   ☐ Oath

Other(Details)

Date Notarized:    Time:

**AM PM**

Document:      Document Date:

☐ Affidavit    ☐ Trust    ☐ Acknowledgement
☐ Mortgage/Deed    ☐ Will    ☐ Power of Attorney
☐ Auto Title    ☐ Claim    ☐ Other: _____

Notary Service Performed at:

**IDENTIFICATION**
Type:

Number:

Issued By:

Expires:

Notes/Comments:

Witness Name/Address:      Witness Signature:

Known Personally:
☐ Yes   ☐ No

**RECORD NUMBER
253**

---

| Name of Signer *(printed)* | Signer's Signature | Fee Charged:$ |
|---|---|---|

Signer's FULL Address      Phone No.

Right Thumb Print
*(When Applicable)*

Notary Service(s) Performed   ☐ Jurat   ☐ Acknowledgment   ☐ Oath

Other(Details)

Date Notarized:    Time:

**AM PM**

Document:      Document Date:

☐ Affidavit    ☐ Trust    ☐ Acknowledgement
☐ Mortgage/Deed    ☐ Will    ☐ Power of Attorney
☐ Auto Title    ☐ Claim    ☐ Other: _____

Notary Service Performed at:

**IDENTIFICATION**
Type:

Number:

Issued By:

Expires:

Notes/Comments:

Witness Name/Address:      Witness Signature:

Known Personally:
☐ Yes   ☐ No

**RECORD NUMBER
254**

---

| Name of Signer *(printed)* | Signer's Signature | Fee Charged:$ |
|---|---|---|

Signer's FULL Address      Phone No.

Right Thumb Print
*(When Applicable)*

Notary Service(s) Performed   ☐ Jurat   ☐ Acknowledgment   ☐ Oath

Other(Details)

Date Notarized:    Time:

**AM PM**

Document:      Document Date:

☐ Affidavit    ☐ Trust    ☐ Acknowledgement
☐ Mortgage/Deed    ☐ Will    ☐ Power of Attorney
☐ Auto Title    ☐ Claim    ☐ Other: _____

Notary Service Performed at:

**IDENTIFICATION**
Type:

Number:

Issued By:

Expires:

Notes/Comments:

Witness Name/Address:      Witness Signature:

Known Personally:
☐ Yes   ☐ No

**RECORD NUMBER
255**

| Name of Signer *(printed)* | Signer's Signature | Fee Charged:$ |
|---|---|---|

| Right Thumb Print *(When Applicable)* | Signer's FULL Address | Phone No. |
|---|---|---|

Notary Service(s) Performed    ☐Jurat    ☐Acknowledgment    ☐Oath

Other(Details)

Date Notarized:    Time:

AM PM

**IDENTIFICATION**

Notes/Comments:

Document:                Document Date:

Type:

☐ Affidavit    ☐ Trust    ☐ Acknowledgement

☐ Mortgage/Deed    ☐ Will    ☐ Power of Attorney

☐ Auto Title    ☐ Claim    ☐ Other: _____

Number:

Issued By:

Notary Service Performed at:

Expires:

**RECORD NUMBER 256**

Witness Name/Address:         Witness Signature:

Known Personally:

☐Yes ☐No

---

| Name of Signer *(printed)* | Signer's Signature | Fee Charged:$ |
|---|---|---|

| Right Thumb Print *(When Applicable)* | Signer's FULL Address | Phone No. |
|---|---|---|

Notary Service(s) Performed    ☐Jurat    ☐Acknowledgment    ☐Oath

Other(Details)

Date Notarized:    Time:

AM PM

**IDENTIFICATION**

Notes/Comments:

Document:                Document Date:

Type:

☐ Affidavit    ☐ Trust    ☐ Acknowledgement

☐ Mortgage/Deed    ☐ Will    ☐ Power of Attorney

☐ Auto Title    ☐ Claim    ☐ Other: _____

Number:

Issued By:

Notary Service Performed at:

Expires:

**RECORD NUMBER 257**

Witness Name/Address:         Witness Signature:

Known Personally:

☐Yes ☐No

---

| Name of Signer *(printed)* | Signer's Signature | Fee Charged:$ |
|---|---|---|

| Right Thumb Print *(When Applicable)* | Signer's FULL Address | Phone No. |
|---|---|---|

Notary Service(s) Performed    ☐Jurat    ☐Acknowledgment    ☐Oath

Other(Details)

Date Notarized:    Time:

AM PM

**IDENTIFICATION**

Notes/Comments:

Document:                Document Date:

Type:

☐ Affidavit    ☐ Trust    ☐ Acknowledgement

☐ Mortgage/Deed    ☐ Will    ☐ Power of Attorney

☐ Auto Title    ☐ Claim    ☐ Other: _____

Number:

Issued By:

Notary Service Performed at:

Expires:

**RECORD NUMBER 258**

Witness Name/Address:         Witness Signature:

Known Personally:

☐Yes ☐No

| Name of Signer *(printed)* | Signer's Signature | Fee Charged:$ |
| --- | --- | --- |

**Signer's FULL Address**      Phone No. | Right Thumb Print *(When Applicable)*

Notary Service(s) Performed   ☐ Jurat   ☐ Acknowledgment   ☐ Oath

Other(Details)

Date Notarized:    Time:    AM PM

Document:      Document Date:

☐ Affidavit    ☐ Trust    ☐ Acknowledgement
☐ Mortgage/Deed    ☐ Will    ☐ Power of Attorney
☐ Auto Title    ☐ Claim    ☐ Other: _____

Notary Service Performed at:

**IDENTIFICATION**
Type:
Number:
Issued By:
Expires:

Notes/Comments:

Witness Name/Address:      Witness Signature:

Known Personally:    ☐ Yes   ☐ No

**RECORD NUMBER 259**

---

| Name of Signer *(printed)* | Signer's Signature | Fee Charged:$ |
| --- | --- | --- |

**Signer's FULL Address**      Phone No. | Right Thumb Print *(When Applicable)*

Notary Service(s) Performed   ☐ Jurat   ☐ Acknowledgment   ☐ Oath

Other(Details)

Date Notarized:    Time:    AM PM

Document:      Document Date:

☐ Affidavit    ☐ Trust    ☐ Acknowledgement
☐ Mortgage/Deed    ☐ Will    ☐ Power of Attorney
☐ Auto Title    ☐ Claim    ☐ Other: _____

Notary Service Performed at:

**IDENTIFICATION**
Type:
Number:
Issued By:
Expires:

Notes/Comments:

Witness Name/Address:      Witness Signature:

Known Personally:    ☐ Yes   ☐ No

**RECORD NUMBER 260**

---

| Name of Signer *(printed)* | Signer's Signature | Fee Charged:$ |
| --- | --- | --- |

**Signer's FULL Address**      Phone No. | Right Thumb Print *(When Applicable)*

Notary Service(s) Performed   ☐ Jurat   ☐ Acknowledgment   ☐ Oath

Other(Details)

Date Notarized:    Time:    AM PM

Document:      Document Date:

☐ Affidavit    ☐ Trust    ☐ Acknowledgement
☐ Mortgage/Deed    ☐ Will    ☐ Power of Attorney
☐ Auto Title    ☐ Claim    ☐ Other: _____

Notary Service Performed at:

**IDENTIFICATION**
Type:
Number:
Issued By:
Expires:

Notes/Comments:

Witness Name/Address:      Witness Signature:

Known Personally:    ☐ Yes   ☐ No

**RECORD NUMBER 261**

| Name of Signer *(printed)* | Signer's Signature | Fee Charged:$ |
|---|---|---|

| Right Thumb Print *(When Applicable)* | Signer's FULL Address | Phone No. |
|---|---|---|
| | Notary Service(s) Performed ☐Jurat ☐Acknowledgment ☐Oath<br><br>Other(Details) | Date Notarized: Time:<br><br>AM PM |
| Notes/Comments: | Document: Document Date:<br><br>☐ Affidavit ☐ Trust ☐ Acknowledgement<br>☐ Mortgage/Deed ☐ Will ☐ Power of Attorney<br>☐ Auto Title ☐ Claim ☐ Other: _____<br><br>Notary Service Performed at: | **IDENTIFICATION**<br>Type:<br><br>Number:<br><br>Issued By:<br><br>Expires: |
| **RECORD NUMBER 262** | Witness Name/Address: Witness Signature: | Known Personally:<br>☐Yes ☐No |

| Name of Signer *(printed)* | Signer's Signature | Fee Charged:$ |
|---|---|---|

| Right Thumb Print *(When Applicable)* | Signer's FULL Address | Phone No. |
|---|---|---|
| | Notary Service(s) Performed ☐Jurat ☐Acknowledgment ☐Oath<br><br>Other(Details) | Date Notarized: Time:<br><br>AM PM |
| Notes/Comments: | Document: Document Date:<br><br>☐ Affidavit ☐ Trust ☐ Acknowledgement<br>☐ Mortgage/Deed ☐ Will ☐ Power of Attorney<br>☐ Auto Title ☐ Claim ☐ Other: _____<br><br>Notary Service Performed at: | **IDENTIFICATION**<br>Type:<br><br>Number:<br><br>Issued By:<br><br>Expires: |
| **RECORD NUMBER 263** | Witness Name/Address: Witness Signature: | Known Personally:<br>☐Yes ☐No |

| Name of Signer *(printed)* | Signer's Signature | Fee Charged:$ |
|---|---|---|

| Right Thumb Print *(When Applicable)* | Signer's FULL Address | Phone No. |
|---|---|---|
| | Notary Service(s) Performed ☐Jurat ☐Acknowledgment ☐Oath<br><br>Other(Details) | Date Notarized: Time:<br><br>AM PM |
| Notes/Comments: | Document: Document Date:<br><br>☐ Affidavit ☐ Trust ☐ Acknowledgement<br>☐ Mortgage/Deed ☐ Will ☐ Power of Attorney<br>☐ Auto Title ☐ Claim ☐ Other: _____<br><br>Notary Service Performed at: | **IDENTIFICATION**<br>Type:<br><br>Number:<br><br>Issued By:<br><br>Expires: |
| **RECORD NUMBER 264** | Witness Name/Address: Witness Signature: | Known Personally:<br>☐Yes ☐No |

## RECORD NUMBER 265

| | | |
|---|---|---|
| Name of Signer (printed) | Signer's Signature | Fee Charged:$ |

Signer's FULL Address                                    Phone No.                    Right Thumb Print *(When Applicable)*

Notary Service(s) Performed ☐ Jurat ☐ Acknowledgment ☐ Oath

Other(Details)

Date Notarized:                    Time:

AM PM

Document:                                                    Document Date:

☐ Affidavit ☐ Trust ☐ Acknowledgement
☐ Mortgage/Deed ☐ Will ☐ Power of Attorney
☐ Auto Title ☐ Claim ☐ Other: _____

Notary Service Performed at:

**IDENTIFICATION**
Type:

Number:

Issued By:

Expires:

Notes/Comments:

Witness Name/Address:                    Witness Signature:

Known Personally: ☐ Yes ☐ No

**RECORD NUMBER 265**

---

## RECORD NUMBER 266

| | | |
|---|---|---|
| Name of Signer (printed) | Signer's Signature | Fee Charged:$ |

Signer's FULL Address                                    Phone No.                    Right Thumb Print *(When Applicable)*

Notary Service(s) Performed ☐ Jurat ☐ Acknowledgment ☐ Oath

Other(Details)

Date Notarized:                    Time:

AM PM

Document:                                                    Document Date:

☐ Affidavit ☐ Trust ☐ Acknowledgement
☐ Mortgage/Deed ☐ Will ☐ Power of Attorney
☐ Auto Title ☐ Claim ☐ Other: _____

Notary Service Performed at:

**IDENTIFICATION**
Type:

Number:

Issued By:

Expires:

Notes/Comments:

Witness Name/Address:                    Witness Signature:

Known Personally: ☐ Yes ☐ No

**RECORD NUMBER 266**

---

## RECORD NUMBER 267

| | | |
|---|---|---|
| Name of Signer (printed) | Signer's Signature | Fee Charged:$ |

Signer's FULL Address                                    Phone No.                    Right Thumb Print *(When Applicable)*

Notary Service(s) Performed ☐ Jurat ☐ Acknowledgment ☐ Oath

Other(Details)

Date Notarized:                    Time:

AM PM

Document:                                                    Document Date:

☐ Affidavit ☐ Trust ☐ Acknowledgement
☐ Mortgage/Deed ☐ Will ☐ Power of Attorney
☐ Auto Title ☐ Claim ☐ Other: _____

Notary Service Performed at:

**IDENTIFICATION**
Type:

Number:

Issued By:

Expires:

Notes/Comments:

Witness Name/Address:                    Witness Signature:

Known Personally: ☐ Yes ☐ No

**RECORD NUMBER 267**

| Name of Signer *(printed)* | Signer's Signature | Fee Charged:$ |
| --- | --- | --- |

**Right Thumb Print** *(When Applicable)*

Signer's FULL Address | Phone No.

Notary Service(s) Performed ☐Jurat ☐Acknowledgment ☐Oath

Other(Details)

Date Notarized: Time:

AM PM

Notes/Comments:

Document: Document Date:

☐ Affidavit ☐ Trust ☐ Acknowledgement
☐ Mortgage/Deed ☐ Will ☐ Power of Attorney
☐ Auto Title ☐ Claim ☐ Other: _____

Notary Service Performed at:

**IDENTIFICATION**
Type:

Number:

Issued By:

Expires:

**RECORD NUMBER 268**

Witness Name/Address: Witness Signature:

Known Personally:
☐Yes ☐No

---

| Name of Signer *(printed)* | Signer's Signature | Fee Charged:$ |
| --- | --- | --- |

**Right Thumb Print** *(When Applicable)*

Signer's FULL Address | Phone No.

Notary Service(s) Performed ☐Jurat ☐Acknowledgment ☐Oath

Other(Details)

Date Notarized: Time:

AM PM

Notes/Comments:

Document: Document Date:

☐ Affidavit ☐ Trust ☐ Acknowledgement
☐ Mortgage/Deed ☐ Will ☐ Power of Attorney
☐ Auto Title ☐ Claim ☐ Other: _____

Notary Service Performed at:

**IDENTIFICATION**
Type:

Number:

Issued By:

Expires:

**RECORD NUMBER 269**

Witness Name/Address: Witness Signature:

Known Personally:
☐Yes ☐No

---

| Name of Signer *(printed)* | Signer's Signature | Fee Charged:$ |
| --- | --- | --- |

**Right Thumb Print** *(When Applicable)*

Signer's FULL Address | Phone No.

Notary Service(s) Performed ☐Jurat ☐Acknowledgment ☐Oath

Other(Details)

Date Notarized: Time:

AM PM

Notes/Comments:

Document: Document Date:

☐ Affidavit ☐ Trust ☐ Acknowledgement
☐ Mortgage/Deed ☐ Will ☐ Power of Attorney
☐ Auto Title ☐ Claim ☐ Other: _____

Notary Service Performed at:

**IDENTIFICATION**
Type:

Number:

Issued By:

Expires:

**RECORD NUMBER 270**

Witness Name/Address: Witness Signature:

Known Personally:
☐Yes ☐No

| Name of Signer *(printed)* | Signer's Signature | Fee Charged: $ |
|---|---|---|

Signer's FULL Address

Phone No.

Right Thumb Print *(When Applicable)*

Notary Service(s) Performed  ☐ Jurat  ☐ Acknowledgment  ☐ Oath

Other(Details)

Date Notarized:          Time:

AM  PM

Document:                                    Document Date:

**IDENTIFICATION**

Type:

☐ Affidavit      ☐ Trust      ☐ Acknowledgement

☐ Mortgage/Deed  ☐ Will       ☐ Power of Attorney

☐ Auto Title     ☐ Claim      ☐ Other: _____

Notary Service Performed at:

Number:

Issued By:

Expires:

Witness Name/Address:          Witness Signature:

Notes/Comments:

Known Personally:

☐ Yes  ☐ No

**RECORD NUMBER**
**271**

---

| Name of Signer *(printed)* | Signer's Signature | Fee Charged: $ |
|---|---|---|

Signer's FULL Address

Phone No.

Right Thumb Print *(When Applicable)*

Notary Service(s) Performed  ☐ Jurat  ☐ Acknowledgment  ☐ Oath

Other(Details)

Date Notarized:          Time:

AM  PM

Document:                                    Document Date:

**IDENTIFICATION**

Type:

☐ Affidavit      ☐ Trust      ☐ Acknowledgement

☐ Mortgage/Deed  ☐ Will       ☐ Power of Attorney

☐ Auto Title     ☐ Claim      ☐ Other: _____

Notary Service Performed at:

Number:

Issued By:

Expires:

Witness Name/Address:          Witness Signature:

Notes/Comments:

Known Personally:

☐ Yes  ☐ No

**RECORD NUMBER**
**272**

---

| Name of Signer *(printed)* | Signer's Signature | Fee Charged: $ |
|---|---|---|

Signer's FULL Address

Phone No.

Right Thumb Print *(When Applicable)*

Notary Service(s) Performed  ☐ Jurat  ☐ Acknowledgment  ☐ Oath

Other(Details)

Date Notarized:          Time:

AM  PM

Document:                                    Document Date:

**IDENTIFICATION**

Type:

☐ Affidavit      ☐ Trust      ☐ Acknowledgement

☐ Mortgage/Deed  ☐ Will       ☐ Power of Attorney

☐ Auto Title     ☐ Claim      ☐ Other: _____

Notary Service Performed at:

Number:

Issued By:

Expires:

Witness Name/Address:          Witness Signature:

Notes/Comments:

Known Personally:

☐ Yes  ☐ No

**RECORD NUMBER**
**273**

| Name of Signer (printed) | Signer's Signature | Fee Charged:$ |
|---|---|---|

| Right Thumb Print (When Applicable) | Signer's FULL Address | Phone No. |
|---|---|---|

Notary Service(s) Performed ☐Jurat ☐Acknowledgment ☐Oath

Other(Details)

Date Notarized: Time:

AM PM

| Notes/Comments: | Document: | Document Date: | IDENTIFICATION |
|---|---|---|---|

Type:

☐ Affidavit ☐ Trust ☐ Acknowledgement

Number:

☐ Mortgage/Deed ☐ Will ☐ Power of Attorney

Issued By:

☐ Auto Title ☐ Claim ☐ Other: _____

Expires:

Notary Service Performed at:

**RECORD NUMBER 274**

Witness Name/Address: Witness Signature:

Known Personally:

☐Yes ☐No

---

| Name of Signer (printed) | Signer's Signature | Fee Charged:$ |
|---|---|---|

| Right Thumb Print (When Applicable) | Signer's FULL Address | Phone No. |
|---|---|---|

Notary Service(s) Performed ☐Jurat ☐Acknowledgment ☐Oath

Other(Details)

Date Notarized: Time:

AM PM

| Notes/Comments: | Document: | Document Date: | IDENTIFICATION |
|---|---|---|---|

Type:

☐ Affidavit ☐ Trust ☐ Acknowledgement

Number:

☐ Mortgage/Deed ☐ Will ☐ Power of Attorney

Issued By:

☐ Auto Title ☐ Claim ☐ Other: _____

Expires:

Notary Service Performed at:

**RECORD NUMBER 275**

Witness Name/Address: Witness Signature:

Known Personally:

☐Yes ☐No

---

| Name of Signer (printed) | Signer's Signature | Fee Charged:$ |
|---|---|---|

| Right Thumb Print (When Applicable) | Signer's FULL Address | Phone No. |
|---|---|---|

Notary Service(s) Performed ☐Jurat ☐Acknowledgment ☐Oath

Other(Details)

Date Notarized: Time:

AM PM

| Notes/Comments: | Document: | Document Date: | IDENTIFICATION |
|---|---|---|---|

Type:

☐ Affidavit ☐ Trust ☐ Acknowledgement

Number:

☐ Mortgage/Deed ☐ Will ☐ Power of Attorney

Issued By:

☐ Auto Title ☐ Claim ☐ Other: _____

Expires:

Notary Service Performed at:

**RECORD NUMBER 276**

Witness Name/Address: Witness Signature:

Known Personally:

☐Yes ☐No